The Master's Healing Touch

JAMES W. ZACKRISON, EDITOR

The Master's Healing Touch

REVIEW AND HERALD® PUBLISHING ASSOCIATION
HAGERSTOWN, MD 21740

The author assumes full responsibility for the accuracy of all facts and
quotations as cited in this book.

This book was
Edited by Gerald Wheeler
Copyedited by Jocelyn Fay and James Cavil
Designed by Patricia S. Wegh
Cover illustration by Harry Anderson
Typeset: 11/12 Garamond 3

PRINTED IN U.S.A.

99 98 97   5 4 3 2 1

R&H Cataloging Service
The Master's healing touch. Edited by James
    W. Zackrison

    1. Health.   2. Healing, Spiritual.
I. Zackrison, James W., ed.

                    261.8321

ISBN 0-8280-1298-9

Contents

Introduction

Many of the miracles related in Scripture deal with a ministry of healing. The Old Testament presents the concept of *shalom,* a Hebrew word embodying the idea of "completeness," or "personal well-being," as an expression of God's will for humanity. *Shalom* also contains a mental component, the complete healing and peace that God brings to the body and soul.

Health is an extremely important issue for Seventh-day Adventists. Admonitions and instructions regarding a healthful lifestyle fill the writings of Ellen G. White. Our health-care institutions and systems span the globe. Vegetarianism and abstinence from harmful substances are components of the lifestyle of most Seventh-day Adventists. In many parts of the world people know the church more for its health message than anything else.

The doctrine of the nonimmortality of the soul is the theological basis for the Seventh-day Adventist interest in health. The human person is a unity, not a compartmentalized body and soul. What affects the mind also affects the body and physical health. And what affects physical well-being shapes spiritual development and the mental state. Good health can only enhance spiritual and mental well-being. The ideal combination is *shalom,* the state of maximum well-being the Lord desires for His followers.

What is a ministry of health and healing? Usually we study health issues from the perspective of the things a person ought to do—or not do—to attain and maintain optimal health. It is also important, however, to study the reasons good health is essential. Why did Jesus spend a considerable part of His ministry healing people? What is the role of prayer in a healing ministry? Is an "herb" packaged as a plant or powder better than the same chemical combination in a pill bottle? Is "natural" healing better than treatment in a hospital or clinic? Should people ever doctor themselves? Is it important to tell people about good health, or is it just a supplementary teaching of the church involving primarily the members? How do the products in a health food store compare with those in the local pharmacy? How does the concept of righteousness by faith relate to an emphasis on proper diet and health care? Are health-oriented teachers and practitioners in reality works-oriented because they are interested in physical, mental, and spiritual well-being, and sometimes quite vocal about their interest?

This book is a companion to a Sabbath school Bible study guide entitled *Healing and Restoration: The Master's Touch.* Written by a team of health professionals, the guide explores the philosophy of health through the eyes of Jesus and His health ministry. Most of the chapters in this book have their basis in a series of study papers prepared by the Health and Temperance Department of the General Conference of Seventh-day Adventists under the title *Health 2000 and Beyond.*

Health education is an ongoing process. It is hoped that the combination of the study guide and this book will be useful as study material for small groups, seminars, health-related events, and discussion groups.

Chapter 1

WHAT MOSES SAYS ABOUT HEALTH AND HEALING

Angel Manuel Rodriguez, Th.D.

What did Moses say about health and healing? In this chapter we will examine the Hebrew term *shalom*, look into the nature of sickness and its causes, including healing, and investigate what Moses says about God as healer and the role of medicine.

SHALOM: WHOLISTIC HEALTH

Biblical scholars generally agree that the Hebrew term *shalom* comes closer than any other to expressing the biblical understanding of health.[1] This is certainly true in the Pentateuch, the first five books of the Bible. We may translate *shalom* as "completeness, soundness," "personal welfare, health," and "prosperity, peace, wholeness, and state of health." The verbal forms of the word stress the ideas of completeness, well-being, and wholeness, thus suggesting a state or situation that fully meets all the needs of a person.

We must understand health in the Pentateuch in very broad categories, because humans are multifaceted beings, and to upset almost any aspect of their personhood affects the wholeness of their lives. To be whole, then, means that they have all their needs satisfied and that their whole organism is functioning in a balanced way within a proper environment. At Creation humans began in a state of *shalom,* or wholeness, but to preserve that condition they must work together with God. Health, understood as *shalom*, requires for its continuation the involvement of the person in his or her own well-being.

THE MASTER'S HEALING TOUCH

Scripture often uses *shalom* as a common greeting generally understood as "peace to you" (Gen. 43:23), but it also has the deeper meaning of "'to be whole, to be complete,' to have physical and spiritual resources sufficient to one's need."[2] To ask about someone's *shalom* means to be interested in their well-being (Gen. 43:27), his or her state of health and quality of life (cf. Gen. 29:6; 43:27, 28).

We see the conceptual content of *shalom* further illuminated through its usage in Genesis 28:20-22. Jacob prays, "If God will be with me and will watch over me on this journey I am taking and will give me food to eat and clothes to wear so that I return safely ["in peace," *shalom*} to my father's house, then the Lord will be my God."* Here the Bible writer views *shalom* to be the result of God's presence in Jacob's life. It includes the ideas of divine companionship, protection, and the provision of food and clothes for Jacob during his journey. *Shalom* thus encompasses a state of physical, mental, and spiritual well-being, enlarging our understanding of health as being wholeness of existence.

The word contains a psychological component as well. Mental health is part of the Old Testament understanding of health.[3] Pharaoh had a dream that impressed him so much that the following morning "his mind {*ruach*} was troubled {*paam*}" (Gen. 41:8). The term *ruach*, usually translated "spirit," often designates the mind as an organ of knowledge, understanding, and judgment. The verb *paam* means "to trouble, disturb." The king seems to suspect that the dream involves future events that may affect him and his kingdom. The fact that he is unable to understand the dream disturbs his mental state, creating anxiety and robbing him of his mental tranquillity. Joseph informs Pharaoh that God will address his concerns and will give him *shalom* "peace" (verse 16). The passage suggests that *shalom* designates an untroubled state of mind characterized by tranquillity.

We cannot separate an individual's *shalom* from the conditions around him or her. Leviticus 26:6 describes the *shalom* of the land almost as a paradise. Its inhabitants live on it free from fear, in "a state characterized by the absence of danger from wild beasts and the sword, when one may sleep at ease,"[4] and they enjoy prosperity (verse 9).

WHAT MOSES SAYS ABOUT HEALTH AND HEALING

PRESERVATION OF HEALTH

As we will discover throughout this book, the Bible views a person as a single unity of life and consciousness in bodily form (Gen. 2:7). Whatever a person experiences, he or she does so as an undivided unity. It is this belief that makes a wholistic concept of health necessary in biblical thinking. The preservation of that state of *shalom* is the dual responsibility of both God and the creature.

DIET AND HEALTH

The very first time God addressed Adam and Eve, His main topic of conversation centered on proper diet (Gen. 1:29). The two newly created persons were not self-existent. To preserve their lives and well-being required in part the consumption of a specific type of food. Obviously, God's intention in assigning food to Adam and Eve was to keep them alive (see also Gen. 6:21).

The diet was a simple vegetarian one. They were to eat "every seed-bearing plant . . . and every tree that has fruit with seed in it" (Gen. 1:29), i.e., grains and fruits. In Genesis 2:17 God forbids Adam and Eve to eat of the tree of the knowledge of good and evil. Notice that although they had the ability to preserve themselves by eating food, the fact that God defined and established the limits of their diet indicates that it is ultimately obedience that maintains their life and wholeness. To reject the divinely set limitations would be tantamount to proclaiming absolute self-sufficiency, and the result would have been the disruption of *shalom* and finally death.

The most significant dietary regulation in the Pentateuch appears in Leviticus 11, the chapter about clean and unclean animals. Is this law just a ritual, or is it interested in what we call hygiene and health? Scholars suggest different theories to explain the origin and purpose of this legislation.[5] Most tend to reject the hygienic/health interpretation, although some still maintain it.[6]

The uncleanness of the animals listed here is fundamentally different from regular ceremonial uncleanness. The animals are permanently or inherently unclean. The ceremonial laws deal only with uncleanness that a person can remove through specific rituals. Any other uncleanness in Leviticus could be acquired through contact with the impure except this one. This emphasizes the uniqueness of this legislation and suggests that it is not ceremonial in the strict sense of the word. Leviticus 11 forbids one to become impure by eating any of the forbidden species. The dietary scheme is a mode of attaining or expressing holiness (verse 44), and to violate this divine command toward holiness is a moral breach (verses 45-47). We should not overlook the obvious fact that this law is about food for human consumption. Scripture introduces it by stating, "Of all the animals . . . these are the ones you may eat" (Lev. 11:2).

Scholars generally accept that "uncleanness" in Leviticus is a metaphor for that which alienates from God and that it is closely related to the concept of death. The most abhorrent source of impurity is a dead body (Num. 19:11). Blood is one of the most common sources of impurity, because it is life running out, extinguishing itself (Lev. 15:19-23, 25-27). The person who is unclean has come in touch with death and is perceived as being in its realm, separated from others and from access to the sanctuary. Ceremonial impurity could be removed by proper rituals enabling the individual to be restored to harmony with God and others. The unclean animals, however, belong to the sphere of death permanently because their uncleanness is permanent. Those who partook of their flesh found themselves in the realm of death. Here we have a clear concern for the well-being, the health of the individual. Violating this law involved three areas of Israelite life: their physical well-being could be affected through diseases; their religious life could be impaired by not having access to the sanctuary; and their social life was interrupted by being separated from others.

HEALTH, OBEDIENCE, AND LONGEVITY

The Pentateuch usually associates health with a long and full life, at the end of which one descends to the tomb "in peace" (Gen. 15:15). Infant mortality may have been very high throughout the ancient Near East, but we have little specific evidence to prove it. It is even difficult to establish the life expectancy of Israel's neighbors. Mummies and other physical remains suggest that in most cases it was not high, because of accident, disease, and general malnutrition. The Egyptians considered the ideal life span to be 110 years, despite the fact that autopsies of royal mummies indicate that even the privileged would most often be dead by age 35.[7]

The Pentateuch reported the life span of the antediluvians as very high, from 777 to 969 years. The life expectancy of the patriarchs, including Moses, was significantly lower, but still high by our standards. The average was 250 years. The wilderness generation had a life span of 60 years, but in general the Israelites seem to have had a life expectancy from 70 to 80 years (cf. Ps. 90:10). By contrast, archaeological evidence suggests a life expectancy of from 18 to 25 years of age for those of the surrounding cultures.

The Lord promised to lengthen the Israelites' life span, a fact stressed repeatedly by Deuteronomy. The promise is that the people will live long in the land of Canaan (Deut. 4:40; 5:16; 11:9), that their days will be prolonged (Deut. 5:33), that they will enjoy a long life (Deut. 6:2), that their days will be many (Deut. 11:21), or that God will give them many years (Deut. 30:20). In every passage, though, longevity depends on obedience to God's commandments. By choosing obedience, the people elect life (verse 19). To be alive is to be able to enjoy a full and healthy life. God preserves the health of His people through His laws, showing that human beings are responsible before God for their own health.

HEALTH AND COMPANIONSHIP

A healthful existence requires human interaction, of being part of the life of other human beings such as friends, relatives, or a spouse. The biblical text states that it was "not good" for Adam to be alone (Gen. 2:18). This indicates absence of wholeness or *shalom*.

HEALING IN THE PENTATEUCH

The Pentateuch recognizes that the ideal state of wholeness God instituted at creation no longer exists. The intrusion of sin into the world altered in a significant way the *shalom* both of the individual and of the created world. Since then sickness and death characterize all human existence.

THE MASTER'S HEALING TOUCH

NATURE OF SICKNESS

How should we understand sickness? What does the Pentateuch mean by it? The biblical writers perceive illness as the first sign of the presence of death in the world of the living. Its power disrupts the *shalom* of God's creation.

The most important Hebrew term for sickness is *halah*, usually translated "to be/become weak, sick, ill." Scholars agree that the verb designates a state of bodily weakness. The vital energy or power has been sapped, and the person finds himself or herself in a condition of weakness or exhaustion. To be sick is to be deprived of fullness of life, of its power and vibrancy, to be in a very special way touched by death. In Hebrew thinking, a sick person is one who is already in the sphere of death (cf. Ps. 88), and unless healing takes place, the person may actually die. In this sense sickness and impurity are practically synonyms.

WHY DO PEOPLE GET SICK?

The ancient Near East usually viewed sickness as resulting from the activity of the gods/goddesses, demons, and even the dead. Sometimes they attributed it to the use of magic by the enemies of the afflicted. Magic and polytheism were so intertwined that dealing with one presupposed dealing also with the other. Even though at times the ancients recognized some natural causes, they still considered the ultimate source of sickness as practically always magic and/or the deeds of the gods.

In the writings of Moses, which were monotheistic and recognize no rival powers equal to God, God describes Himself as the ultimate cause of all disease (Deut. 32:39). When inflicting sickness, He may use heavenly messengers (Gen. 19:11), the dust (Ex. 9:8, 9), serpents (Num. 21:4-9), or even clean meat (Num. 11:33; cf. Ps. 78:31), but He is always identified as the ultimate source.

Often the Pentateuch portrays disease as resulting from God's rejection of the sin of His people. In some cases the connection between disobedience and sickness is almost one of cause-effect. The account of Miriam, struck with leprosy because of her sin, describes God as actively involved in the process (Num. 12:1-13). In a number of cases God inflicted sickness on non-Israelites. Seeking to protect Abraham and his wife, God struck the house of Pharaoh on two different occasions with a disease that affected the whole household (Gen. 12:17; 20:17). One of the most powerful instruments God used to defeat the Egyptians and liberate His people was sickness (e.g., Ex. 9:8, 9).

In other cases the Lord brings sickness on His people to discipline them after they have violated the covenant (e.g., Lev. 26:16, 25; Deut. 28:21, 22, 27-29). It is His tool to educate them, to show them clearly that life and health exist only within the covenant relationship. By breaking the covenant, His people enter the world of sickness and death.

Associating sickness with sin internalizes the cause of sickness, making it not just a physical problem, but a spiritual one. This indicates that sickness affects the whole person and not just one aspect of his or her being.

According to the Pentateuch, not all diseases result from sinful behavior, however. Blindness, in the case of Isaac, was a symptom of old age (Gen. 27:1). Sarai, Abraham's wife, was barren (Gen. 16:1), but the text makes no indication that it was a punishment from God. However, Jacob ascribed Rachel's infertility to God (Gen. 30:2); but again Scripture does not identify any immediate cause, e.g., sin. The handicapped come under God's protection rather than under His curse (Lev. 19:14). Accidents or fights can result in wounds making the person sick (cf. Ex. 21:18, 19). Too much work is not good for the person, because it will wear him or her out, affecting the individual's well-being (Ex. 18:18). Here sickness results from intemperance. It is highly probable that the Israelites considered even these "chance" situations to be the result of God's permissive will (cf. Ex. 21:13).

GOD'S ROLE AS HEALER

Scholars usually translate the Hebrew verb *rapha* as "to heal, to be healed, restored." Its usage in the Pentateuch makes it crystal clear that in Israel the one responsible for healing was the Lord. Soon after the Israelites left Egypt, God revealed Himself as "the Lord, who heals you" (Ex. 15:26). His claim rests on the fact that only He is an all-powerful God: "There is no god besides me. I put to death and I bring to life, I have wounded and I will heal, and no one can deliver out of my hand" (Deut. 32:39). God as healer means that there is no other God like Him who is in complete control of life and health. God's healing power goes beyond the restoration from physical sickness and encompasses the restoration of *shalom*.

HEALING AND PREVENTIVE MEDICINE

How does God bring healing? In the Pentateuch healing rarely results from God's miraculous intervention. It appears to take the form of preventive medicine, apparently based on the theological conviction that God does have power over sickness. That being the case, healing, properly speaking, comes to play a secondary role. The Lord can protect His people from the power of disease itself.

Nevertheless, we do find cases of healing. Healing sometimes takes place through intercessory prayer—as we would expect, because the Lord controls disease and healing. Abraham prayed for the restoration of the health of Abimelech and his household, and God healed them (Gen. 20:17). Isaac prayed for Rebekah, who was barren, and the Lord answered his prayer (Gen. 25:21). Moses interceded on behalf of his sister, Miriam, and God healed her leprosy (Num. 12:13, 14).

The sacrificial system seems to have played a significant role in the restoration and preservation of the spiritual and mental well-being of the Israelites. Moral and religious failures, whether accidental or intentional, created deep feelings of guilt, upsetting the person's psychological balance. Through the sacrificial system the individual experienced God's forgiving grace and the restoration of fellowship with God (e.g., Lev. 4:35).

Preventive medicine seems to have played an important role in the laws of uncleanness dealing with blood contamination and diseases (Lev. 12:4, 5). Quarantine was important in dealing with cases of uncleanness and diseases (Num. 5:2). The ancient Near East employed quarantine for epidemics or contagious diseases. The ancient Mesopotamian Asqudum advises King Zimri-Lim to stay in the city of Terqa and not to continue on his way to

Sagaratum because the land "was contaminated" with an epidemic. Whenever a servant of the king or the queen got sick, he or she was immediately isolated and moved to new quarters.

Isolation had also an important prophylactic function in the case of leprosy (Leviticus 13; 14). The leprosy mentioned in Leviticus does not seem to be what we call today Hansen's disease (Lev. 13:47-52, KJV). Scholars have argued that modern leprosy was unknown in the ancient Near East during the Old Testament period. They base their argument on the fact that paleopathological studies have not been able to identify a true case of leprosy in the biblical lands before the sixth century A.D.[8] However, in 1980 excavation in a cemetery in Lower Egypt uncovered human bones showing clear evidence of leprosy. Archaeologists dated the remains to the Hellenistic period, c. 200 B.C.

The Hebrew term *saraath,* translated "leprosy," is a medical term. Scholars have suggested it might refer to such conditions as psoriasis, seborrheic dermatitis, fungus infection of the skin, patchy eczema, and pityriasis rosea. Another scholar comments that the symptoms listed in Leviticus 13 seem to apply more to the communicable diseases characterized by skin rash, such as measles, smallpox, scarlet fever, etc.[9] However, it is practicably impossible to identify clearly the diseases described in chapter 13, and thus it may be safer to keep the designation as broad as possible and to include Hansen's disease. Quarantine or permanent isolation, in this case, would have prevented the spread of the disease.

ROLE OF MEDICINE

Medical practice seems to have been well developed in Egypt and in Mesopotamia. Nevertheless, medicine and magic were closely intertwined. It has been stated that in Egypt most of the rational means of treatment were inefficient. Magic was indeed the one element common to almost the whole prophylactic armory of the ancient Egyptians.

Rational medicine was probably known in Israel, but the Pentateuch provides little evidence of it. An interesting case appears in Exodus 21:18, 19. A man hurts another during a fight, confining him to bed. According to the law, the one who struck the blow "must pay the injured man for the loss of his time and see that he is completely healed" (verse 19). The passage suggests that Israel may have had physicians who charged for their services. What is implicit here is that the work of God as healer and the work of humans as physicians are not incompatible.

Healing in the Pentateuch involves the restoration of the whole person and includes the restoration of the surrounding environment to its fertility and peace. Scripture emphasizes God's healing power because of Israel's monotheistic faith. Other cultures might have one or more gods of healing or medicine, but Israel believed in the existence of only one God. The Pentateuch suggests that when medicine was practiced within the constraints of God's sovereignty, within the covenant faith, it was indeed compatible with the view that God is after all the healer of His people.

CONCLUSION

We must understand health in the Pentateuch in broad terms. The noun *shalom* defines it in terms of wholeness. Health includes such ideas as prosperity, security, and the spiritual, physical, mental or emotional, and social well-being of the person. In order for that individual to function properly, the environment itself must have *shalom*.

Preserving that state of wholeness was the responsibility of both God and human beings. God gave them specific instructions on how to preserve their wholeness—proper diet, work, rest, companionship—but humans had the power to reject or accept the instruction.

We must remind ourselves that healing as the restoration of wholeness to humans and the environment continues to be a task of divine proportions. Humility must always characterize our involvement in the healing process.

---

*Bible references in this chapter are from the New International Version.

[1] K. Seybold, *"Chalah,"* *Theological Dictionary of the Old Testament (TDOT)*, ed. G. J. Botterweck and H. Ringgren (Grand Rapids: William B. Eerdmans, 1974), vol. 4, p. 401.

[2] Joseph P. Healey, "Peace: Old Testament," *Anchor Bible Dictionary,* David Noel Freedman, ed. (New York: Doubleday, 1992), vol. 5, p. 206.

[3] See Reuven P. Bulka, "Mental Health: Biblical and Talmudic Directives," *Koroth* 9 (1988): 30-41; and J. V. Kirmier Wilson, "Mental Health of Ancient Mesopotamia," in

Diseases in Antiquity, eds. Don Brothwell and A. T. Sandison (Springfield, Ill.: Charles C. Thomas, 1967), pp. 723-733.

⁴A. Bauman, *"Harad," TDOT,* vol. 5, p. 170.

⁵For an evaluation, see Walter Houston, *Purity and Monotheism* (Sheffield: Sheffield University Press, 1993), pp. 68-123; for an Adventist evaluation of those theories, see Angel Manuel Rodriguez, "Levitico 11: Los animales puros y los impuros," *Ministerio Adventista* 34 (marzo-abril 1986): 20-23; William H. Shea, "Clean and Unclean Meats" (Silver Spring, Md.: Biblical Research Institute, 1988), pp. 13-18; and G. F. Hasel, "Clean and Unclean Meats in Leviticus 11: Still Relevant?" *Journal of the Adventist Theological Society* 2 (1991): 107-111.

⁶P. D. Craigie, *The Book of Deuteronomy* (Grand Rapids: W. B. Eerdmans, 1976), p. 231; R. K. Harrison, *Leviticus* (Downers Grove, Ill.: InterVarsity Press, 1980), pp. 12-31; Donald J. Wisernan, "Medicine in the Old Testament World," in *Medicine and the Bible,* ed. Bernard Palmer (Exeter: Paternoster Press, 1986), pp. 13-83; and R. Laird Harris, "Leviticus," in *The Expositor's Bible Commentary,* ed. Frank E. Gaebelein (Grand Rapids: Zondervan, 1990), vol. 2, pp. 568, 569.

⁷Helmer Ringgren, *"Chayab," TDOT,* p. 326; and A. Malamat, "Longevity: Biblical Concepts and Some Ancient Near Eastern Parallels," *Archiv für Orienforschung* 19 (1982): 215.

⁸Richard N. Jones, "Paleopathology," *Anchor Bible Dictionary,* vol. 5, p. 65.

⁹Harris, pp. 501-654.

Angel Manuel Rodriguez is an associate director of the Biblical Research Institute, Silver Spring, Maryland.

Chapter 2

THE COMPASSION OF JESUS

James W. Zackrison, D.Miss.

Compassion is a familiar word to most people, usually understood as a synonym for mercy or feeling pity for someone because of their physical, economic, or moral situation. The common understanding of the term in Jesus' time we find expressed in James 2:12, 13: "Speak and act as those who are going to be judged by the law that gives freedom, because judgment without mercy will be shown to anyone who has not been merciful. Mercy triumphs over judgment!"* This interpretation led to a high degree of public display, especially in giving money (alms) to help the poor. People perceived showing mercy, or compassion, and making sure everyone knew about it, as a way of escaping judgment. It became a mechanical activity, not a heartfelt empathy. James, of course, placed the statement within a Christian context: "But the wisdom that comes from heaven is first of all pure; then peace-loving, considerate, submissive, full of mercy and good fruit, *impartial and sincere*" (James 3:17).

Jesus considered compassion to be far more intimate and intrinsic than the common understanding. "So when you give to the needy, do not announce it with trumpets, as the hypocrites do in the synagogues and on the streets, to be honored by men. I tell you the truth, they have received their reward in full" (Matt. 6:2). In a parallel passage in Luke 12, Jesus' advice was: "But rather seek ye the kingdom of God; and all these things shall be added unto you. . . . Sell that ye have, and give alms; provide yourselves bags which wax not old, a treasure in the heavens that faileth not, where no thief approacheth, neither moth corrupteth" (verses 31-33, KJV).

THE MISSION OF THE MESSIAH

The Messiah's mission on earth was one of justice, but a justice based on compassion. Ellen White states: "He looked with compassion upon those who were being corrupted, murdered, and lost" (*The Desire of Ages*, p. 36). Jesus' compassion ran so deep that when He looked on sinners, "their very misery and sin made them only the more the objects of His compassion" (*Christ's Object Lessons*, p. 186).

Jesus often quoted from Isaiah 61 (see *The Desire of Ages*, pp. 236, 237, 242). The passages He cited clearly outline His mission, and in Luke 4 He used them to announce publicly that He was the Messiah (see verse 21).

These passages (Isaiah 61; Luke 4) contain eight elements:

    (1) the Messiah anointed by the Lord;

    (2) good news preached to the poor;

    (3) the brokenhearted healed;

    (4) liberty proclaimed to the captives;

    (5) release announced for the prisoners;

    (6) sight restored to the blind;

    (7) the year of the Lord's favor proclaimed;

    (8) the day of God's vengeance announced.

Some commentators see the various elements as having primarily a spiritual application. In this sense, good news to the poor would mean to the poor in spirit, people requiring salvation. The captives and prisoners would be those bound by sin, who need release from the grip of Satan. Others see the verses as a call for social justice for those who are literally poor, blind, and in prison.

JEWISH SOCIETY AND THE CALL FOR JUSTICE

Jesus uses Isaiah 61 to call for justice and declare salvation. When we think of the poor, we usually do so in terms of financial poverty, but it is not only lack of material resources that makes people outcasts. Jewish society ostracized anyone with a major disease because of the common belief that all disease was a punishment from God for personal or inherited sin. Thus the blind were pariahs, but to Jesus they were among the "poor" He came to save.

Tax collectors like Matthew were among the wealthiest people in the community, but by Jewish standards they were outcasts, unworthy of salvation, because of their collaboration with the Roman government. Many Jews did not consider Samaritans as even part of the human race. They were certainly "prisoners" in terms of social fellowship. And the widow who gave only two mites, the smallest monetary unit available, was certainly "captive" to the injustice of favoritism shown to people who donated large offerings and made a great show of what they gave. It was with these "poor" that Jesus spent most of His time. Probably the popular concept of God's wrath kept Jesus from reading the phrase in Isaiah 61—"and the day of vengeance of our God" (verse 2)—when He spoke in the synagogue in Nazareth.

Jesus' treatment of people from all classes of society and His never-failing love, sympathy, and concern for the outcasts and the oppressed, were among the strongest evidences of His Messiahship. Paul would later remark: "The saying is sure and worthy of full acceptance, that Christ Jesus came into the world to save sinners" (1 Tim. 1:15, NRSV).

THE COMPASSION OF JESUS[1]

The compassion of Jesus is so profound that no illustration fully captures it. Ellen G. White compares it to "a golden chain, the mercy and compassion of divine love, that is passed around every imperiled soul. The Lord declares, 'I have loved thee with an everlasting love; therefore with lovingkindness have I drawn thee' (Jer. 31:3)" (*Christ's Object Lessons,* p. 202).

Jesus' healing ministry reflected His deep compassion for those in need. Matthew includes a number of instances in which persons called out to Jesus for mercy. Each time they made such a plea, He responded positively, healing the person.

The Gospels use a particular Greek word to describe Jesus' compassion, *splagchnizomai.* In the common language of the day the word meant "the inner parts," and was actually used to describe an upset stomach. So it became an expression that meant a person had been moved to the very heart and soul of his or her being.

THE COMPASSION OF JESUS

The words for "mercy" and "compassion" occur more often in Matthew than in the other Gospels. *Mercy* in Matthew is consistently the plea that persons make to Jesus to receive healing (cf. Matt. 9:27-31; 15:21-28; 17:14-20; 20:29-34). Often such a plea combined with an expression of faith in Jesus as the Messiah, the "Son of David." Jesus consistently responded to these pleas with healing. At times the biblical writers expressed Jesus' feelings toward a crowd or sufferers with the term compassion. When He felt compassion, He consistently came to the aid of those in need.

However, Matthew's emphasis on mercy and compassion does not end with recounting Jesus' experience. Showing mercy becomes a requirement for all believers, as illustrated in such passages as the Beatitudes (Matt. 5:7—"the merciful . . . will receive mercy" [NRSV]) and the parable of the unforgiving servant (Matt. 18:33—"Shouldn't you have had mercy on your fellow servant just as I had on you?"). This, indeed, highlights another teaching of the healing ministry of Jesus in Matthew: the necessity of a changed life for having received mercy and healing yourself.

Mark also writes about Jesus' compassion. In compassion He touches a leper to heal him (Mark 1:40-45), feeds hungry and leaderless crowds (Mark 6:34; 8:2), shows mercy to a distraught demoniac (Mark 5:1-20), and heals an anxious father's demon-possessed son (Mark 9:14-29). Mark's focus on miracles often presents the pathos of the human situation, in which people have suffered for long periods of time. Jesus' acts of healing relieve the tension built up by the depth of trouble the individuals have faced.

John focuses on Jesus' expression of compassion in the way He heals the royal officer's son despite the man's initial unbelief. He meets the soldier's pathetic cry, "Sir, come down before my child dies!" with the words of authority and peace, "You may go. Your son will live" (John 4:49, 50). Another glimpse of Jesus' compassion appears in His healing of the man at the pool of Bethesda who He knew had "been there a long time" (John 5:6, NRSV). But the most explicit expression of Jesus' compassion occurs in chapter 11, which recounts His love for Lazarus, Martha, and Mary. Jesus risks His life to return to raise His friend, the sisters present their pathetic plea, "Lord, if you had been here, my brother would not have died" (11:21, 32), and finally, He weeps.

EXAMPLES OF COMPASSION AND MERCY

Compassion is love in action. The outstanding example in Jesus' ministry is the parable of the good Samaritan in Luke 10. It was because the Samaritan showed compassion that Jesus termed him "good." As far as His contemporaries were concerned, there could never be such a thing as "good" Samaritans. In this case, however, Jesus translated the law of love into the business of life. The Samaritan's focus was on the need of another. He directed his attention to the point of greatest suffering. Jesus applied the parable by declaring, "go and do likewise" (verse 37).

From a negative perspective, Jesus taught a significant lesson about compassion with the parable of the unmerciful servant. The debtor's master, Jesus said, "took pity on him" (Matt. 18:27), the same concept as compassion. The debtor, however, did not feel the same compassion for someone who owed him only a few units of money. Judgment fell on him because he did not demonstrate compassion himself. Compassion, then, works both ways. If it is applied, it is a Christian virtue. If it is withheld, it becomes a reason for judgment. True compassion is not just an idea, it is an action. Correct behavior is definitely part of true compassion.

Speaking of the attitude of the religious leaders and their business ventures in the Jerusalem Temple, Ellen G. White writes: "The priests and rulers were called to be the representatives of God to the nation; they should have corrected the abuses of the temple court. They should have given to the people an example of integrity and compassion. Instead of studying their own profit, they should have considered the situation and needs of the worshipers, and should have been ready to assist those who were not able to buy the required sacrifices. But this they did not do. Avarice had hardened their hearts" (*The Desire of Ages,* pp. 156, 157).

The other outstanding example of compassion in action in the Gospels is the story of the prodigal son. "But while he was still a long way off," the record reads, "his father saw him and was filled with compassion for him; he ran to his son, threw his arms around him and kissed him" (Luke 15:20).

Modern-day Compassion

In today's world, how do people respond when they think of an Adventist hospital, medical doctor, dentist, nurse, or para-professional? We could add to the list lawyers, auto mechanics, or any professing Christian. Would they say he or she "is a compassionate person"?

"The best technology does not necessarily communicate compassion," writes Tom Shepherd. "Indeed, sometimes the big machines (why are they always so cold to the touch?) bespeak distance and antisepsis. The parable of the unmerciful servant in Matthew 18 brings home a message for our day. It is those who have received the mercy of God in their lives who ought to show it to everyone they contact."

Incarnational Ministry

Showing compassion and mercy, in the final analysis, is a gift of grace. Those who have experienced the grace of Christ, who have really known the forgiveness and freedom He alone grants, they are the people of grace. The Holy Spirit touches the chords of their hearts to know what gracious word to express, the gentle touch to give, the prayer of hope, the sacrifice of time that says, "I know," "I care," and "I am with you in this time of need." Such people move the world; they cannot be forgotten. Theirs is a ministry of healing, mercy, and compassion.

Incarnational ministry is the spirit of compassion, caring, and acceptance shown by Jesus in His ministry. It is the model our own ministry should follow. When Jesus went back to heaven after the resurrection, He passed on to us the responsibility to continue the ministry He had initiated. We are the "music" of the gospel that people hear. Much of what they learn about Jesus they acquire from our attitudes and actions.

Jerry Cook, a pastor who was trying to build a caring, loving congregation, tells about a phone call he received one day:

"You know what you are out there?" the voice on the other

end said. "You're nothing but a bunch of garbage collectors."

What He meant was that Jerry Cook's church was trying to rehabilitate broken-down people. The more he thought about it, the more Jerry realized that the man was right. They were garbage collectors, just as Jesus was. Jesus, he realized, finds us as garbage and recycles us into sons and daughters of God.

He told the story in church one morning, and after the service a man came up to him and said, "You know, I am a real garbage collector. That's my job. For 10 years we dumped garbage in a landfill. We moved to a new one a while ago, and you know what the old one is now? A beautiful park."[2]

HOW INCARNATIONAL MINISTRY WORKS

Incarnational ministry is putting the gospel into action. Assume you are sitting in prayer meeting and someone mentions that a person in the congregation just lost his job. They request prayer for the member and want to ask the Lord to help the individual find a job. The Lord, however, has already promised to help in time of need, so it is redundant to ask Him to do what He has already said He will do. Then someone asks, "What does this person do?"

"He's an auto mechanic."

"Do we have any auto mechanics in the congregation?"

"Yes."

"Who will contact them and see if they have any leads that might help this member?"

"Who will mobilize the church to make sure that this family has food on the table, etc., while we help him find a job?" another says.

Now we are in the business of ministry. Now our prayer for the Lord's help is a prayer for aid in accomplishing some specifics of ministry. Now someone can pray, for instance, that the church will be led to find the right people who can be of assistance. Compassion takes time, dedication, energy, and determination. It is faith in action.

I can hear someone say, "The man probably lost his job because he was lazy, inept, and hard to get along with. Why should the church waste its time?" Maybe so. Then again, there's the prodigal son. And the woman who bathed Jesus' feet was not exactly the paragon of virtue. Jesus didn't just say "Nice day, isn't it?" to the woman at the well (John 4) who had her own set of problems!

God summons you and me to an incarnational ministry as modeled by Jesus. Even when seemingly rejected, Ellen G. White tells us, the Syrophoenician woman saw beneath the apparent refusal of Jesus "a compassion that He could not hide" *(The Desire of Ages,* p. 401). That is the ultimate Christian goal, a compassion that cannot be hidden.

RECIPROCAL LIVING

There is another aspect to the compassion of Jesus that we often overlook. Jesus was not only personally compassionate, He admonished His disciples in all ages to develop a corporate ministry of compassion (John 17:23). We accomplish it through applying a set of admonitions built around the Greek word *allelon.* The word means "one another." The "one another" statements in the New Testament reflect most areas of life. A truly compassionate and caring congregation will attempt to demonstrate these characteristics in its ministries, attitudes, interpersonal relationships and dealings, and congregational life in general.

Compassion embodies the Messiah's ministry. For Jesus, compassion was second nature. It was part of His daily life and ought to be the same with us. Healing ministries, health education, helping people to a better life, are all part of a ministry of compassion. That is the call to real discipleship.

---

*Bible references in this chapter are from the New International Version unless noted otherwise.

---

[1] Some of the material on the compassion of Jesus comes from the original of the article by Tom Shepherd that appears in edited form as chapter 5 of this book.

[2] Jerry Cook with Stanley C. Baldwin, *Love, Acceptance, and Forgiveness* (Ventura, Calif.: Regal Books, 1979).

James Zackrison is the director of the Sabbath School/Personal Ministries Department of the General Conference of Seventh-day Adventists, Silver Spring, Maryland.

Interrelationships	Mutual edification	Mutual service	Negative commands
Love one another	Build up one another	Be servants to one another	Do not judge one another
Receive one another	Teach one another	Bear one another's burdens	Do not speak evil of one another
Greet one another	Exhort one another	Be hospitable to one another	Do not murmur against one another
Have the same care for one another	Admonish one another	Be kind to one another	Do not bite and devour one another
Submit to one another	Speak to one another in songs and psalms	Pray for one another	Do not provoke one another
Forbear one another			Do not envy one another
Confess your sins to one another			Do not lie to one another
Forgive one another			

Chapter 3

SHOULD WE PRAY FOR THE SICK?

Jon Dybdahl, Ph.D.

The Bible mentions many instances of healing through prayer, and the apostle James leaves us with specific instructions: "Pray for each other so that you may be healed" (James 5:16, NIV).

Ellen White subscribed to the biblical view: "It has often been my privilege to pray with the sick. We should do this much more often than we do. If more prayer were offered in our sanitariums for the healing of the sick, the mighty power of the Healer would be seen. Many more would be strengthened and blessed, and many more acute sicknesses would be healed" (*Selected Messages,* book 3, p. 295).

The major concern of this chapter is how prayer and faith relate to healing. The basic question involves prayer for physical and mental healing, since most probably already believe that prayer for spiritual matters is valid.

The major questions are: (1) Do prayer and/or faith have a role in the treatment of medical and physical needs? (2) If the answer is yes, what is that role, and how does it mesh with the overall Adventist concept of healing?

The Western Adventist Church and the dominant medical community have largely neglected spiritual healing in general and prayer for the healing of the physically and mentally ill in particular. The church should make it a high priority to develop a theology of healing prayer and to institute the practice of such prayer as a vital, integral part of our ministry to those in need.

THE MASTER'S HEALING TOUCH

EVIDENCE OF NEGLECT

As far as I know, no scientific statistical studies have been done on the amount of prayer offered in connection with medical practice or ministerial work in the Seventh-day Adventist Church. In spite of this lack, I think that if we examined our own experience and our sense for what goes on in our churches and medical institutions, most would agree that we probably offer little actual prayer for physical and mental healing.

Not many years ago I was teaching a course called Biblical Perspectives on Healing to a group of nurses in an Adventist institution of higher learning in the United States. I taught in a classroom used by the School of Nursing adjacent to a major Seventh-day Adventist medical institution. We talked at length about prayer for the sick, and I suggested that the students begin to practice what they had learned in class in their work at the hospital. I felt, however, that before I made the assignment I should check with the chaplain. Calling him on the phone, I talked with him at length. It was obvious from the beginning that he was uneasy with my proposal, but in deference to me as a friend he did not give me a flat no. Instead he said, "I'll send word with the students next week." The conditions laid down were so stringent that I backed off, not wanting to make it a major issue. The man was a godly man and was interested in spiritual ministry to people, but prayer for healing simply made him nervous. I have discussed prayer for the sick with many Adventist ministers and again sensed an uneasiness.

WHY WE NEED HEALING PRAYER

Some may feel such neglect is good and safe. Why do we need a renewal of healing prayer in the church? I suggest four major reasons.

1. The historical reason. This refers to both the history of the church and the present situation in which we find ourselves. First, as we look at the past, early Adventism had a widespread belief in and practice of prayer for healing. Anyone who reads widely in Ellen White's writings, particularly those from the early days, will find this so.

What it means is that my call for renewal of interest in healing prayer in Adventism is not new. Ellen White never saw the establishment of hospitals and sanitariums as something in opposition to belief that God could, in fact, work directly to bring healing in people's lives. What has simply happened is that over a period of time we have lost one of the original emphases in the church.

2. The theological reason. Besides historical reasons, we have very good theological reasons for an emphasis on prayer for healing.

First is the doctrine of spiritual gifts, or, as early Adventism called it, the "perpetuity of spiritual gifts." Certainly the list of spiritual gifts found in 1 Corinthians includes the gift of healing along with those of teaching, apostleship, and prophecy. Early in its history Adventism made the definite decision that the gifts that God promised to the church in the Apostolic Era were not temporary. The gift of the Holy Spirit did not exist at one period of time and then be withdrawn, but the Spirit continued to give gifts to enable the church to minister in a powerful way for her Lord. Healing is included and meant more than learned techniques of medicine. Although we may not have practiced it, it is there in our theology, and we shouldn't forget it.

Second, our doctrine of humanity implies it. We believe people exist as integrated units. Without the body and the breath there is no living soul. The life God gives manifests itself in the material, physical body. Both are necessary for life. The whole person is important. You don't simply treat one part—you deal with the whole, unified entity.

3. The pastoral reason. Prayer for healing needs renewed emphasis in the church for pastoral reasons. It seems clear that in many parts of our world the single model of the dominant therapeutic medicine has failed to minister to people's deep needs. Because we care about the people in our world and church, we need to be concerned about those needs. We need a ministry that goes beyond medical treatment practiced in the secular sense.

Not only that, we have in our own *Minister's Manual* instruction for an anointing prayer service. For many the service has become like last rites for Catholics. What was originally meant to be quite commonly used to minister to people has become something employed only in serious cases as a last resort. We should be serious about this rite or be honest and leave it out of our publications.

4. *The missiological/evangelistic reason.* In the New Testament healing went right along with the preaching of the Word. The church did not preach the Word without accompanying signs and wonders, and signs and wonders were always followed by an explanation and an exposition of the Word of God.

Most world religions participate in spiritual healing. Many Christian groups believe strongly that Jesus Christ has the ability to heal people, and along with the spoken message goes the active message of God's power to operate in our lives. Unless we who claim to be believers and followers of the Word get these two aspects back together again, we are going to be left behind by those who preach not only in word but in deed.

FALSE EMPHASES AND PATHS OF RENEWAL

Seven major ideas, or emphases, have led to the current neglect of prayer for healing. We need to alter or abandon the concepts. Therefore, with each of the false ideas or emphases I have paired a truer or more correct emphasis or concept that can help us restore healing prayer to the place that it should have in our midst and can lead to renewal.

MONOCAUSAL VERSUS MULTICAUSAL MODEL

False concept: many believe that in the area of healing everything is basically monocausal, meaning that one explanation or cause dominates a particular area of life. The dominant medical model claims that it has the one basic explanation for all disease, something to do with germs or viruses, and a cure by some kind of medicine, treatment, or surgery. Any other kind of explanation is suspect and either must be seriously questioned or simply appears to be helpful because of a placebo effect.

Lest we be too hard on this particular model of medicine, the monocausal model has also affected most types of alternative medicine. Chiropractors, herbalists, psychologists, reflexologists, faith healers—all believe, in general, that the one thing they do will cure all diseases and make all people well.

This monocausal model makes it extremely difficult for a person who accepts the modern dominant medical model or any other non-religious model to believe that prayer can have anything other than a marginal effect. It brings a sense of cognitive dissonance. If you believe things are monocausal, how do you integrate a second cause?

True concept. In opposition to the monocausal model is a multicausal model. The human person and healing are so complex and so deep that in fact different models and causes may be operating at the same time. Instead of seeing something from one viewpoint, we can recognize that multiple causes and factors may relate to the case. Those causes are not in opposition to each other, but can in fact be integrated.

Even a cursory reading of Ellen White's writings shows us that she saw no conflict between following what she called natural remedies, or scientific medicine, and prayer for the sick, thus modeling the kind of ministry talked about in the Scriptures (see *Medical Ministry,* pp. 28, 29).

CHARISMAPHOBIA VERSUS CHARISMAFFINITY

False concept: the second kind of viewpoint that has contributed to the demise of healing prayer is what I call charismaphobia. Since many charismatics pray for the sick, our fear of them leads to a fear of prayer for healing.

Adventists have many beliefs in common with charismatics: that the gifts remain; that God can really work in everyday life; that the Holy Spirit will continue and will in fact be manifest even more strongly as time comes to an end. One need only to read the original documents of Adventism to find that not only did prophecy operate in the early days of our church, but other gifts, such as healing, tongues, interpretation of tongues, etc., took place in those days. We find also that other phenomena that are not directly mentioned in Scripture but that are part of the charismatic movement occurred regularly in Adventism, such as being slain in the spirit, shouting out in exultation to God, and so forth.

True concept: as opposed to this charismaphobia, which fears anything connected with healing because it is related to the charismatic movement, I suggest the viewpoint that I call Charismaffinity. Adventism has an affinity, a similarity, to the charismatic movement. It does not mean a wholehearted acceptance of everything that the charismatic movement professes. Although such an approach does pose dangers, yet I think we need to be honest and recognize that in many ways our theology fits more with charismatic theology than it does with the traditional dispensational evangelicals who do not see God as working powerfully through spiritual gifts. This would allow us to avoid the great fear that we feel anytime somebody talks about prayer for healing.

MODEL EMPHASIS VERSUS MOTIVE EMPHASIS

False concept: a model refers to the overall approach utilized. What I mean by a model of healing prayer is the whole package used by a particular practitioner of prayer for healing. Unfortunately, the most spectacular and often the most obnoxious models are the ones that appear on television. Many people simply feel uneasy praying for the sick because the only models they have seen may have been those who by their action and by their portrayal of healing caused the viewer to reject the whole process.

True concept: what I suggest in opposition to what I call model emphasis is what I would term motive emphasis. What many people are doing is using a valid motive, i.e., a desire to heal by prayer, in a model or system that we simply cannot identify with. What we need to do is look at the motive and develop our own models for practicing healing prayer. Just because some faith healers shout or command God, or make a spectacle, does not mean that we must conduct all healing prayer according to this model.

Many other healing models exist, most of them not nearly as well known, that fit much more closely with the kinds of things we feel comfortable with. A mild, quiet model of prayer for the sick may match our customary worship and prayer style. Because the motive of using prayer on behalf of the sick is biblically valid, we must develop our own models or ways that suit the personality and character of our lives and our churches.

OVEREMPHASIS ON FAITH VERSUS EMPHASIS ON LOVE

False concept: some have overemphasized or distorted the roles of faith and individual power in the area of healing prayer. Along with this stress on faith has usually come a focus on the individual—a kind of charismatic, out-front, public healer—and on the power of God to heal. This complex of faith, individual, and power is not necessarily wrong, but we have concentrated far too much on this area.

In the miracles of Jesus Christ faith is a factor in healing in many instances. But Scripture reports many other instances that do not mention faith or treat it as an important element in the healing. I've read numerous books about healers—from Mary Baker Eddy to Kathryn Kuhlman to John Wimber—and in the stories of the people healed I find time and again dedicated, faith-filled Christian people who are not healed. On the other hand, unbelievers, people dragged to the meetings who have no belief or faith at all, go and are touched by God's power.

This whole complex of faith, individual, and power has caused us to shrink from prayer. We are afraid we will lose faith or be blamed for lack of faith if we pray for a person and nothing happens. If we do not get blamed, then the person will be blamed and feel even worse after the prayer, because to their sickness of body or mind is now added the spiritual sickness of guilt for being of such little faith that God cannot touch and heal them.

True concept: as opposed to what I call the faith/individual/power emphasis, I suggest a community and obedience emphasis, that is to say, prayer for the sick should occur because we love people. It should take place in the community in which not one charismatic, dynamic leader prays, but in which many regular people reach out to pray for others. It happens in the context of obedience, in which we obey Bible commands to pray.

This emphasis has freed me to pray for the sick in a way that I was not able to do before. I can simply tell people, "I am praying for you because God loves you and because He has called us to love you, and through this prayer I want our love and His love to be revealed to you, and I want you to know that people in the church love you and are trying to obey Jesus."

We don't know if our faith is great or small, but we are obeying what Jesus Christ has asked us to do, so we do it in that context. That releases us and them from guilt. We don't spend a lot of time analyzing their or our faith. As we love and obey, faith grows naturally.

CULTURAL CAPTIVITY VERSUS BIBLE RECEPTIVITY

False concept: many of us are prisoners of the dominant world-view of our twentieth-century culture. The Western world has adopted an enlightenment-scientific viewpoint that puts great emphasis upon the physical world around us and the ability to conduct repeatable scientific experiments. It leaves little room for the activity of God. Not all cultures have this view, but it is becoming more and more a pervasive worldwide outlook.

Contemporary medicine is a part of this cultural captivity. We can explain disease apart from anything related to God. Time and again I have met people who simply are reluctant to talk about prayer, ashamed to speak about God, because they are afraid of being ridiculed and being thought unintelligent and anti-intellectual. The bright people are the ones who believe science, while those who accept religion are the weak, the uneducated, and the weird. Whether we like to admit it or not, this attitude affects the way we look at healing prayer.

True concept: to counter this viewpoint, I suggest biblical receptivity. If we take the Bible seriously, we cannot but recognize that Scripture assumes and operates on the whole issue of prayer for the sick and the ability of God to work in people's everyday lives. What, in fact, happened to me was that I came full circle. Trained in the intellectual rigors of this Western system at a high level, I was taught to go back and read the original documents of my faith. In reading them, I saw how much this kind of healing, this kind of divine action, was a part of what took place. It forced me to ask myself, "Do I really believe this or do I not? What in my worldview has made me blind to seeing this?" I find the biblical worldview opposed to the contemporary cultural worldview, and I have to take a stand.

TRUTH DEFENSE VERSUS MISSION OFFENSE

False concept: for a long time the church has had what I call a truth-defense emphasis. The essence of our religion has been some kind of definable doctrinal truth. That truth was special and was to be defended. It was not based on experience, emotion, feeling, or mystical experiences, but was some kind of rational, explainable, expressible thing that was to be defended before anyone who raised questions about it.

Nothing is wrong with truth and nothing is wrong about defending it. What has happened in the Adventist Church, however, is that because we have been small and because some of our beliefs have been viewed as strange by the culture outside (for example, the Sabbath and some of our dietary practices), we have tried to be superrational. Since society has seen faith healing itself and prayer for the sick as a fringe endeavor, we have shied away from it simply because we don't want to be viewed as a part of that group. We have enough that is different about us already and don't need any more.

True concept: I don't suggest that we abandon truth, but in opposition to this truth emphasis we need to stress what I call mission offense. We need to worry less about a rational defense of what exists and more about our mission to the world. As Adventists we need to switch gears from being simply a defensive team to being an offensive one.

Thus we need to ask such questions as How can the secular mind be convinced that God is alive? How can people who see no evidence of the divine in their lives come to believe that God is active in our world? Prayer for healing fits with that emphasis. God is more eager to show Himself than we have ever believed, and we need to seek to allow Him to act.

PERSONAL VERSUS PRINCIPLE

False concept: we have overstressed the personal, ethical, and theological integrity of the one praying. I have heard many people comment, "Well, so-and-so could never really pray for the sick, because you know he is not a Sabbathkeeper," or "We know that so-and-so's life is not perfect, so how can he truly pray for the sick?" Not only does that seem overly judgmental, but also it makes people afraid to pray for the sick. Can only perfect people pray for healing? That leaves out everyone except Jesus.

THE MASTER'S HEALING TOUCH

True concept: it is, in fact, a principle of Scripture that prayer for people in the name of Jesus Christ is going to have an effect. I don't think Peter was perfect. Certainly Paul had areas in which he had to grow in his life, yet we don't deny the fact that both men could pray for the sick. A person being able to pray for the sick doesn't mean we accept their theology and their ethics. On the other hand, they may, in fact, be more obedient to some biblical commands than we are.

CONCLUSION

Certainly a renewed emphasis on healing prayer would bring questions. Abuses and problems will occur, but the writings of Scripture and Ellen White make it an essential and integral part of the full ministry of God's church to the world. We need to be seeking ways to make that kind of ministry the key part of our lives and work that it should be.

Instead of following the models of other people, we can develop our own. I believe we need several major types of models. We must have public models that can be used in church services and evangelistic meetings as well as private models that individuals or small groups can practice. And we need pastoral models that minister to church members and missionary models that come into play with nonbelievers. As a church and as individuals we will learn much as we try various ways to minister through healing prayer. In the process, God will change and renew us, and His healing power will be manifest to a hurting world.

Jon Dybdahl is professor of missions at the Seventh-day Adventist Theological Seminary, Berrien Springs, Michigan.

Chapter 4

KEEPING BODY, SOUL, AND SPIRIT TOGETHER

Patricia Jones, Ph.D., R.N.

The word "whole" comes from the Greek word *holos,* meaning to embrace all, a whole that works together in harmony. Wholeness is a synonym for completeness, being all together, and perfection. Other attributes or characteristics of wholeness include balance, energy, and inner strength.

"Caring for the whole person" and "making man whole" are common phrases in Seventh-day Adventist vocabulary. Does the Seventh-day Adventist Church believe that the word "healing" refers primarily to the physical human body, or does it also apply to mental, emotional, and spiritual health? Since we believe that the human being is an integrated whole and does not have a separate "soul" immune to those things that affect us in the world around us, we also believe that all the dimensions of a human being work together and are affected by one another. Commitment to healing and educating the whole person—helping both sick and well individuals become whole in body, mind, and spirit—is the reason we have health education programs in the church.

With our deep interest in wholeness, we might assume that Seventh-day Adventists have a well-understood and complete theology or theory of health as wholeness. Though we talk a great deal about wholeness and care of the whole person, in actuality we continue to study, treat, and develop the mental, physical, and spiritual aspects of our being separately. It appears that we subscribe to the idea of wholeness without developing a theory or even the concept of wholeness itself.

THE MASTER'S HEALING TOUCH

Western philosophy and science in general do not say much about wholeness. Eastern thought and practices, along with some other traditions, however, do emphasize the concept. Those seeking a truly wholistic perspective of health often turn to them for help. Those of us with a particular interest in wholeness need to accept the challenge of developing the concept from a Western tradition and to suggest a model for promoting wholeness in human beings.

FROM DUALISM TO WHOLISM

Systematic study of the human being as an organism with separate physical, mental, and spiritual components originated with a philosopher named René Descartes in the seventeenth century.[1] His approach, commonly called dualism, led to a remarkable increase in scientific knowledge of the physical and psychological dimensions of the human being, but it neglected the wholistic view of persons.

The Judeo-Christian faith provides a strong foundation for developing a wholistic view of human beings. Monotheism, the worship of one God, helps to bridge the gap in understanding the role of a higher power in the creation and ongoing life of created beings—a gap that polytheistic traditions cannot bridge. Monotheism can also assist us in understanding better how body and spirit are integrated—the physical and spiritual aspects of our being. However, in spite of the potential enriching wholism could offer us, we have not tapped its resources, and even our Christian understanding of the wholistic nature of human beings remains too limited.

WHOLENESS IN THE HEALTH SCIENCES

One of the earliest health-care professionals to focus on the whole person was a Swiss physician named Paul Tournier.[2] Tournier called attention to the fact that though we know more about the human body than ever before, medical science has lost the sense of the person as a whole. "No matter how much we know about the chemico-physical processes in the living organism," he writes, "it doesn't help in understanding the mystery of life which resides not in the parts but in the whole."[3]

KEEPING BODY, SOUL, AND SPIRIT TOGETHER

Nurse scientist Martha Rogers has developed a theory about how the various parts of a human being integrate with one another.[4] She says that human beings are unitary in nature and therefore we must treat and study them wholistically. Her propositions about the unitary nature of human beings cause us to think twice about the nature of health and wholeness. Nurse scholars, for instance, wrestle with these questions and are developing appropriate methodologies for nursing as a human science. This means reexamining some of the traditional ways of doing things and then moving on to study and treat human beings wholistically.

THE NATURE OF WHOLISTIC PERSONS

Tournier pictures the interacting components of the human being—body, mind, psyche, and spirit—as a triangle in which the various elements touch and influence one another. The great mystery, he says, is in understanding the power that integrates the system so that each person functions as a whole. This power, says Tournier, resides in the point of intersection at the center of the triangle, representing the human spirit. The spirit is the core and essence of the person, the integrating factor that gives meaning to the body, the psyche, and the mind.

I have adapted Tournier's model to reflect the openness of the human system and the integration of its various dimensions. I refer to these dimensions as the physiological, psychological, sociocultural, and spiritual variables—all of which are in a constant process of development throughout life. And I agree with Tournier's description of the human spirit as the essence of the person and the integrating factor for wholeness. As the spirit communicates and permeates the entire system, the less fragmented and more integrated it becomes. We see this illustrated by the pervasive influence of the spiritual component on the other dimensions. The human spirit is the sensitive core, both powerful and vulnerable, capable of generating energy and bringing the system together. At the same time it is vulnerable to insult. As reported by Bill Moyers in his book and video series on healing and the mind, the remarkable influence of the inner spirit on the healing processes is an example of its power. For example, the immune system works less efficiently when a person feels depressed, demonstrating the person's inner vulnerability and its effect on health.

The human spirit is particularly sensitive to the Holy Spirit, the primary way through which divine power heals and integrates the person. The more the human spirit is open to the power and influence of the Divine, the more dynamic the process of integration and the greater one's potential to experience healing and wholeness.

This description of the nature of wholistic human beings supports the idea that although all dimensions touch and affect one another, the spiritual dimension has a more direct and permeating influence. It also shows us that we are not human beings trying to be spiritual, but spiritual beings trying to be human. Therefore, treating the spirit of the person offers much potential for healing.

NATURE OF WHOLENESS

Wholeness includes many factors that do not require physical completeness or freedom from illness. For example, the amputee, the quadriplegic, the chronically or terminally ill, may still experience inner harmony and wholeness. As Wilber Alexander says: "Wholeness includes living with the limitations as well as finding new levels of growth."[5] Some of the factors essential for wholeness include the ability to change (adaptability), readiness for change, the ability to communicate and trust, and the drive to find meaning or spiritual awareness in life. Wholeness leads to healing and growth, improved quality of life, peace, joy, meaning, and the strength to let go of life when the moment comes.[6] Such consequences can serve as experiences in personal wholeness. Other experiences could involve a sense of keeping things together, the ability to persevere, productivity, and the spiritual energy to mobilize whatever personal resources are still available to us.

DEVELOPING A DEFINITION

Is wholeness a feeling, a condition, a process, or an experience? Ewing suggests that individuals are continuously reconstituting themselves into new selves in response to both internal and external forces, implying a continuous process.[7] She also suggests that wholeness is a fleeting experience, although at times it may feel like it goes on forever.

Wholeness is the process of dynamic exchange of energy between the various dimensions of the human being. It also connects the dimensions between one human system and another, or between the human spirit and divine power. We can describe wholeness by its attributes, such as balance and harmony. Wholeness is both process (something that is always going on) and outcome (something that actually happens in experience).

Ewing further suggests that much of what we describe as wholeness in Western thinking reflects a view of self that is itself part of the culture.[8] In the West we view self as autonomous—each person is responsible for themselves, and fenced in. I do my thing, you do yours. Most non-Western cultures experience the self by what happens in a person's surroundings. What happens to someone else affects me also. A definition of wholeness, therefore, needs to be relevant to all cultures and allow for the context of each culture.

The following definition allows for variations in both health status and culture: *wholeness is the experience of feeling inner connectedness, integrated functioning, and power to realize one's potential.*

THEORETICAL PARADIGMS

One theoretical concept, or model, that presents a wholistic view of the human being is Von Bertalanffy's general systems theory.[9] The first principle in this theory states that in all systems the whole is greater than the sum of the parts. A house is more than the bricks, lumber, and glass that make it up. A book is far more than paper and ink. The second is that change in any one part affects the whole. We can easily understand and recognize the second principle in health science when, for example, exercise and emotions affect the brain and ultimately the immune system.[10] The first principle, however, is a greater challenge. This principle of the whole being greater than the sum of the parts helps us recognize the interplay among all the human dimensions, but still leaves us with the elusive challenge of how to explain wholeness and how to study and treat persons wholistically.

David Bohm,[11] a London professor of theoretical physics, describes his view of the world as an undivided whole, a continual play and counterplay of events and processes rather than of physical entities. All of reality, Bohm suggests, is an unending process of movement and of opening up. Why things get fragmented and don't stay together, he says, is more subtle and difficult to discover than even those findings that lead to new discoveries in science. Wilber Alexander describes the whole process as a journey.[12]

Bohm observed that we should understand reality as process, an indefinable totality of flowing movement, the act of becoming itself.[13] In the same way, he describes wholeness as both process and content, with movement and flow as primary. Wholeness, then, is an ongoing development of reality, with our experiences as part of that reality, and therefore is both process and outcome. It is a flow of energy within the individual, connecting and integrating all our human dimensions. Also it is the flow of energy and interaction between an individual human being and the world outside of him or her (the environment), and ultimately with the source of all energy, God Himself.

If any one word helps most to describe human wholeness, it is connectedness: connectedness and integration among the various dimensions of our being, connectedness with other humans and with the world around us, and above all, connectedness with a higher power than ourselves. Connectedness empowers growth and integration, and connectedness is life in its fullest sense—both human life now and eternal life in the future.

ELLEN G. WHITE AND WHOLENESS

Ellen White refers to wholeness in two ways: as wholeness in the service of God[14] and as holiness and perfection of character.[15] The first implies wholeness of purpose in dedication to Christian service and consecration of the heart and life to Christ. In the second, she says holiness and perfection of character are wholeness to God, implying that wholeness is not possible without perfection of character. I once heard a helpful description of perfection: perfection is not a condition, but a connection. We have already described wholeness as connectedness. When we understand both perfection and wholeness in terms of being connected with divine power, we more clearly grasp Ellen White's references to wholeness.

STUDYING WHOLENESS AND WHOLISTIC HUMAN BEINGS

Science has gained new insights into the connections between the mind and body, and the effect of positive emotions on the immune system and therefore on healing.[16] Such findings offer convincing evidence of the reality of integrated human functioning. If wholeness is an experience, to examine it we need to know how to study experiences. Bohm explained that in studying wholeness you cannot separate the one doing the observing from the one being observed.[17] Treating the whole person often calls for ways of doing things that specifically apply to certain dimensions of the human being and that serve to benefit and strengthen the whole being. We need to identify and study more wholistic concepts. For example, illness is more than disease or sickness, health is more than merely the absence of disease, and "care" means more than just getting well. Other things we need to think about are the effect of wholeness on pain, comfort, healing, recovery, energy, adaptability, hope, peace, forgiveness, and joy.

A MODEL FOR PROMOTING HEALTH AND WHOLENESS

If wholeness means connecting all the various aspects of a person together, helping energy to flow between the dimensions of a person, and if as a result of this flow healing and the fullest development of the person's potential is possible, health professionals should be concerned how we can make all this happen. If the human being is first of all a spiritual being, and the spirit is the integrating factor, working with and nurturing a person's spirit is a major way of promoting wholeness by all health professionals, not only chaplains and pastors. The challenge is to understand how we can achieve wholeness in those who are extremely fragmented, especially the chronically or terminally ill, as, for example, people with Alzheimer's disease.

Wholistic caring includes doing things that strengthen and mobilize the energy of each human dimension and focuses on whatever will promote communication, connection, and integration. Using resources outside of the individual, especially other human systems and divine power, is also important. We must mobilize and reinforce an individual's strengths, empowering him or her to act purposefully in regard to his or her own health and growth toward wholeness.

One of the biggest barriers to integration and wholeness is what we call established patterns of fragmentation. Adults often have strongly developed walls between the dimensions of their being that inhibit the flow of energy between them and thus limit their integration. People build these walls for protection or out of fear, sometimes because of their social surroundings, or because of individual belief systems. Overcoming such barriers may require a process of "unfreezing," which usually begins with a new awareness of the need for change itself. This may result from new understandings or emotional insights, a crisis, or simply a change in circumstances. It can also result from a caring health professional who helps the person change, get well, and grow. This way the fragmented person can experience wholeness, the chronically ill can have improved quality of life, and the terminally ill can experience peace and strength of spirit to heal relationships and to let go of life.

For many years I have been developing what I call an *effective energy empowerment* model for health and wholeness.

THE EFFECTIVE ENERGY MODEL

Few individuals fully develop their health potential or experience wholeness to the extent to which they are capable. But people feel better when they can mobilize energy, or inner strength, to achieve good health. Such energy is waiting to be generated in each person, and since it is wholistic, all dimensions of a person will influence whether it happens or not. The human system interacts continually with the environment to exchange energy. Similarly, interaction with the Creator is a constant source of new energy and power. Interaction and connection with these sources of support serve as both energy resources and as aids to release the individual's own energy potential. Health professionals are resource persons, enhancing people's abilities to meet their own needs and to mobilize the necessary additional resources to achieve their greatest health potential.

What kind of energy exchange are we talking about? Take the example of unmet needs that cause stress. Identifying the relationships between the different factors putting pressure on us enables us to change the situation. Change in one variable will alter still another. Picture a triangle in your mind. One side represents human needs, and the other adaptability or the ability to change. The base of the triangle represents the effective energy to put the two sides together. As the two sides interact, they produce new outcomes, represented by the base of the triangle. Any change in the sides of the triangle will modify the base. We call the base "effective energy," because human nature is changeable and people can choose to use and develop their human potential. Effective energy doesn't just mean that people are more energetic and move around a lot. It refers to their ability to participate purposefully in life, using all their faculties to develop their health potential. A definition of effective energy is that "energy currently available to an individual that can be mobilized, controlled, and directed toward goal achievement."[18] An increase in effective energy means the person feels as though they can do something about whatever they are experiencing. They can change things. Empowered, they can achieve both a higher level of health and well-being, and a higher quality of life.

---

[1] Alexis Carrel, *Man, the Unknown* (New York: Harper & Row, 1935); Paul Tournier, *The Whole Person in a Broken World* (New York: Harper & Row, 1964).

[2] Tournier, *ibid.*

[3] *Ibid.,* p. 37.

[4] Martha E. Rogers, *An Introduction to the Theological Basis of Nursing* (Philadelphia: F. A. Davis Co., 1970).

[5] Wilber Alexander, "Some Musings on Wholeness" (unpublished paper, Loma Linda University, 1991).

[6] P. Jones and A. I. Meleis, "Health Is Empowerment," *Advances in Nursing Science,* 1993, pp. 1-14.

[7] K. Ewing, "The Illusion of Wholeness: Culture, Self, and the Experience of Inconsistency," *Ethos* 18 No. 3: 251-278.

[8] *Ibid.*

[9] L. von Bertalanffy, "The History and Status of General Systems Theory," in G. J. Klir, ed., *Trends in General Systems Theory* (New York: John Wiley & Sons, 1972), pp. 1-41.

[10] Norman Cousins, *Head First: The Biology of Hope* (New York: E. P. Dutton, 1989);

C. Pert, "The Chemical Communicators," in Bill Moyers, *Healing and the Mind* (New York: Doubleday, 1993).

[11] David Bohm, *Wholeness and the Implicate Order* (London: Routledge & Kegan Paul, 1980).

[12] Alexander.

[13] *Ibid.,* p. 48.

[14] Ellen G. White, "A Divine Leader," *Signs of the Times,* Dec. 20, 1905.

[15] ———, "Christ Our Pattern," *Youth's Instructor,* Oct. 13, 1892; "Doers of the Word," Nov. 5, 1896.

[16] Cousins; Pert.

[17] Bohm.

[18] P. Jones, "Effectiveness Through Adaptation," *Research-oriented Clinical Papers,* Sigma Theta Tau International Monograph Series, vol. 3.

Patricia Jones is a professor in the Graduate School and the School of Nursing, Loma Linda University, Loma Linda, California.

Chapter Five

YOUR FAITH HAS SAVED YOU: A THEOLOGY OF HEALTH AND HEALING IN THE CANONICAL GOSPELS[1]

Tom Shepherd, Ph.D., P.H.

The Gospels are factual, historical narratives of the life of Jesus. However, they are more than this, for the writers all express theological concerns through the way they present characters and events. The stress placed on one element or another, the way the story develops, the way the authors describe characters, what they say, how the stories are arranged—these factors and many others work together to weave a theology of the narrative.

MATTHEW

In Matthew Jesus performs 14 specific healings or resurrections.[2] The writer also provides numerous summaries of His healing work, which impresses upon the reader the idea that the Lord healed many.[3] In fact, the healing summaries are so numerous and the miracle stories so integral to the Gospel's narrative, that it is quite plain that healing is a major theme of Matthew's depiction of Jesus.

The healing ministry of Jesus in Matthew has at least three points of emphasis. The first is that the miracles show He is the Messiah. We see the evidence of this especially in such miracles as the healing of the two blind men (Matt. 20:29-34) with the double use of the Messianic title "Son of David" and the appellation "Lord" repeated three times.[4] Also, the last miracle scene in Matthew occurs in the Temple (Matt. 21:14-16), with Christ healing "the blind and the lame." The children call Him "Son of David." When the religious leaders object, Christ responds with the words of Psalm 8:3: "From the lips of children and infants you have ordained praise" (NIV).

The second focus of the Matthean healing miracles is the compassion Jesus expressed through healing. The words "mercy" and "compassion" occur more often in Matthew than in any of the other Gospels. *Mercy* in Matthew is consistently the plea that people make to Jesus to receive healing.[5] Often such a plea combines with a declaration of faith in Jesus as the Messiah—"Son of David." Jesus consistently responds to these pleas for healing.

The third focus of Matthew's theology of health and healing is the necessity of a changed life for having received mercy and healing. In Matthew 11:20-24 Jesus castigates the cities that witnessed the majority of His healing but did not repent. The gift of grace requires a transformed life. This linkage between healing and a changed life, between belief in Christ and repentance, is rooted in the biblical doctrine of the unity of a person. We do what we are. "A good tree produces good fruit" (Matt. 7:17, CEV).

MARK

Mark reports 13 healing miracles of Jesus and four summaries of His healing work.[6] The miracle stories in Mark have a way of bringing out the pathos of human experience, which serves to highlight Jesus' healing power and at times give indications of how or why He heals. The Gospel writer often relates the history of the persons seeking help, frequently an account of degeneration and extended suffering.[7] The stories often contain delays or intervening circumstances that heighten the tension concerning the suffering and the hope of cure. The demons argue with Christ over the cure (Mark 5:6-12), the woman with the hemorrhage touches Christ from behind for healing (verses 27-34), Jairus's daughter dies as a result of the delay over the healing of the woman (verses 35-43), and a father nearly loses his chance for his son's cure when his lack of faith stands between him and healing (Mark 9:22-29).

These stories grip the heart with their pathos. Yet the focus is always the same: the question of the authority and power of Christ and faith in Him. The pathos, the questions, the pauses and seeming failures, all concentrate the reader's attention on Jesus and the sick person's dependence on Him. Can He work the miracle? Can He overcome the demons? Is He the Christ? Mark is not afraid to place Jesus on the line. The questions receive their answers. He is the Christ, but in a way quite different from human expectations.

Central to Jesus' healing ministry in Mark is its Christological significance. The miracles are tied to the Gospel's revelation and secrecy theme. When Jesus heals a demoniac (Mark 1:23-28), the evil spirit cries out that He is the "Holy One of God" (RSV) (revelation). Jesus, however, orders the spirit to be quiet. "Be quiet! . . . Come out of him!" (NIV) (secrecy). The pattern repeats itself a number of times in the Gospel (see Mark 1:32-34; 3:9-12; 5:21-43; 7:31-37).[8] Why did Jesus order the secrecy? One clue appears in Mark 7:36, 37, in which, having healed a deaf and mute man, Jesus commands silence about the miracle. Mark then relates: "But the more He did so, the more they kept talking about it. . . . 'He has done everything well. He even makes the deaf hear and the mute speak!' " (NIV).

Mark indicates that the secret cannot be hidden—it is meant for revelation. Jesus' miracles are revelation that fulfill a Christological role, pointing out that He is the Christ. That's why 11 of the 13 miracles occur before the central Christological confession in Mark 8:27-30. They serve to focus the attention of the reader upon one of Mark's two central questions: Who is Jesus? The question is the center of focus of Mark 1:1-8:30. Once Mark has sounded the crucial Christological confession in Mark 8:27-30, the focus of the Gospel shifts. The new question is What does messiahship mean? The second half of the Gospel explains that the messiahship of Jesus, so different from the expectation of His day, is one of suffering and death.

Another emphasis of the miracles in Mark is to express Jesus' compassion. In compassion He touches a leper to heal him (Mark 1:40-45), feeds hungry and leaderless crowds (Mark 6:34; 8:2), shows mercy to a distraught demoniac (Mark 5:1-20), and heals an anxious father's demon-possessed son (Mark 9:14-29).

LUKE

The healing miracles of Jesus are more numerous in the

Gospel of Luke than in any other. The book records 17 healing miracles and seven summaries of His ministry of healing.[9]

A key passage for understanding the healing ministry of Jesus in Luke is the sermon in Nazareth (Luke 4:16-21). Jesus quotes from Isaiah 61:1, 2: "The Spirit of the Lord is on me, because He has anointed me to preach good news to the poor. He has sent me to proclaim freedom for the prisoners and recovery of sight for the blind, to release the oppressed, to proclaim the year of the Lord's favor" (NIV). His Nazareth sermon constructs an intimate connection between the proclamation of Jesus and His acts of healing, a relationship that continues throughout His ministry.

In conjunction with the important theme of joy and release, two other main points of emphasis occur in the healing ministry. First, the miracles act as signs of Christ's authoritative power as the Messiah. By His miracles Jesus conquers Satan's realm. On the Sabbath Christ releases a woman bound for 18 years by Satan (Luke 13:10-17). His miracles show that the finger of God is at work in the midst of the people (Luke 11:14-23). The extension of His ministry through the 12 and 72 throws Satan's realm into further disarray (Luke 9:10, 11; 10:17-22). Satan is clearly the foe and Christ decisively the victor. Again and again Christ's authoritative power impresses the people and they praise God for His great deliverance (Luke 4:31-37; 5:17-26; 6:17-19; 13:10-17; 18:35-42).

The other focus of the Lucan healing miracles is the compassion and sympathy of Jesus for sufferers. He has sympathy for the widow of Nain and raises her son (Luke 7:11-17). Graciously He heals 10 lepers who cry out for mercy even though only one returns to give thanks, a Samaritan (Luke 17:12-19).

JOHN

The Gospel of John presents only four healing miracles.[10] Although John has fewer miracles, he develops their significance in great detail. The healing miracles form part of the signs that demonstrate that Jesus is the Christ, the Son of God (John 20:30, 31). The Bible writer links them to one of the central themes of the Gospel—belief. Three of the miracles emphasize the faith of those who receive the blessing of healing: the son of the king's officer (John 4:46-54), the man born blind (John 9:1-41), and the raising of Lazarus (John 11:1-46).

Other aspects of the healing stories in John attract our attention, for instance, the cause of disease. In John 9:1, 2 the disciples question Christ concerning the origin of blindness. They assume that it is a result of sin. Jesus does not reject this viewpoint altogether, but He expresses the higher result to be achieved through the miracle He is about to perform—the demonstration of the glory of God, another of the Gospel's major themes. John repeats the same concept in the story of Lazarus (John 11:3, 4).

Two of the healing miracles John specifically links with the Sabbath: the cure of the paralyzed man at the pool of Bethesda (John 5), and the restoration of sight to the blind man (John 9).

SIGNIFICANT THEMES IN THE GOSPELS

Among the multitude of data that the Gospels present on health and healing in the ministry of Jesus, we notice some recurrent and central themes.

Evidences of Messiahship. The Gospels agree that the healing ministry of Jesus is one of the important signs that He is the Messiah. Matthew emphasizes the way in which Jesus' miracles fulfill the Old Testament prophecies of Isaiah. Many persons who call on Jesus for help use Messianic terminology or the title "Lord." Their faith in Him serves as a necessary ingredient in their healing.

Mark also presents the miracles as Christological proof, something we clearly see illustrated in the fact that the vast majority of the miracles appear before the central Christological confession of Mark 8:27-30. The Bible writer connects the miracles with the secrecy/revelation theme. The demons recognize Christ when He commands liberty and release for those possessed. The miracles reveal His power and authority and challenge the reader to consider with the disciples, "Who is this? Even the wind and the waves obey him" (Mark 4:41, NIV). It leads the reader to confess faith that Jesus is the Christ.

Luke contains similar emphases, but presents Jesus as the Christ based upon the sermon in Nazareth in chapter 4. Jesus quotes Isaiah 61:1, 2, and the passage serves as a model for His healing ministry. The Isaiah passage joins healing with the proclamation of the gospel. Together they produce not only profound awe but also great joy among the people. Christ conquers the realm of Satan and sets his captives free. The finger of God is at work saving His people.

Though John records fewer healing miracles, he more fully develops their significance. Again the central role of the miracles is to illustrate that Jesus is the Son of God. The Bible writer presents a progressive revelation of who Jesus is through the developing reactions of the people. The book prominently emphasizes the importance and centrality of belief. The Christological claims in John are perhaps the strongest of any in the Gospels. Jesus' declarations about Himself and His crowning miracle of raising Lazarus declare Him unmistakably to be the Son of God. With the reaction of unbelief that grows from Jesus' confrontation with the leaders, the miracles also lead inevitably and inexorably to the cross.

Thus the evangelists produce a rich tapestry concerning the significance of Jesus' miracles. They tie their significance as signs of His Messiahship to Old Testament passages that point to the healing and saving power of God. Furthermore, those who call upon Jesus in faith and receive healing become, almost without fail, examples of discipleship. On the other hand, the religious rulers, threatened by the power and meaning of the miracles, almost consistently reject them as a revelation of the Messiah, going so far as to link Jesus with Beelzebub, plot His arrest, and turn Him over to the Romans for crucifixion.[11]

The unity of the person. The biblical concept of the unity of the human being appears in each of the Gospels.[12] The basic idea, rooted in the Creation story of Genesis, is that a person is an indivisible whole of body and spirit.

As a result of being a unit rather than a physical body temporarily inhabited by an immortal soul, a human being's inner life finds expression in actions.[13] Matthew especially portrays the consequences of this doctrine. In Matthew 25:31-46 Jesus depicts the great judgment scene. The Master bases His judgment upon the past actions of those who stand before Him. Judgment here clearly rests on deeds. This is not to say that Matthew teaches righteousness by works.[14] But all of the Gospels contain the principle that what one is on the inside necessarily finds expression on the outside.[15] As Jesus said: "Make a tree good and its fruit will be good, or make a tree bad and its fruit will be bad, for a tree is recognized by its fruit. You brood of vipers, how can you who are evil say anything good? For out of the overflow of the heart the mouth speaks" (Matt. 12:33, 34, NIV). The life of faith requires living in submission to God's will, revealing in one's life the reality of an inward experience.

Faith and healing. It is important to note how the sick approached Christ. Two findings are especially significant. First, the vast majority of Jesus' healings are for those who either ask for help or have someone ask for them.[16] The few healings in which it does not happen involve demoniacs (who cannot ask) and persons healed in the presence of opponents, in which case the confrontation between Jesus and these leaders becomes the focus of the narrative.

The second important finding is the role of the individual's faith in the healing. Jesus often speaks words of peace to the individual: "Your faith has saved you" (see Matt. 9:22; Mark 5:34; 10:52; Luke 7:50; 8:48; 17:19; 18:42). Indeed, the Synoptic Gospels often link words of faith with Christ's miracles. He comments on the person's faith or notes its presence. Unbelief blocks His miracle-working power (cf. Mark 6:5, 6). Belief and unbelief are major themes in John, and he ties his miracle stories to these themes. Thus for healing to occur the sick must come to Christ in faith.

Jesus' compassion. Compassion manifest to those in need is typical of Jesus the Messiah. His miracles in response to the appeal of faith relieve the suffering of multitudes, bring relief to those burdened with years of pain and discouragement, and raise up those lost to death. The overwhelming need of humanity ringing like a sorrowful bell is met by a depth of concern and mercy that turns the funeral march into a parade of joy.

APPLICATIONS

The Gospel realities were meant to be infused into daily life. They present a challenge to the status and value systems of the modern world. The influence of culture, education, and political systems is so powerful in our life and so pervasive that we often do not recognize the presuppositions upon which we base our actions, presuppositions often in conflict with the message of the gospel.

Applying the theology of health of the Gospels to daily life is not an easy task, because of both the distance between our culture and that of Jesus' day, and the reticence we have to change.[17] However, it is the task every disciple of Jesus must undertake.

The gospel necessarily modifies the life, both inward and outward. Healing of the body influences the mind, and healing of the soul influences the daily life.

Jesus' wonderful miracles of healing were signs that show Him to be the Christ. The question is how this translates into the healing ministry of Christians today. First, we can clearly say that Christian healing is not limited to those in the health professions. The example of the paralytic in Mark 2 illustrates this well. Jesus healed him of his sins before He cured his physical ailment. As His disciples we can bring spiritual deliverance.

The compassion Jesus showed should permeate the lives of all Christians. A nurse friend of mine related the story of his working in an emergency department one evening during a rush of patients. The staff shunted the less critical cases to the end of the waiting list. One of them was a patient returning for the dressing of a burn. My friend was tired and harried. He began to remove the dead skin and dress the wound to the cries of the patient. Her family entered the cubicle and began denouncing my friend for his insensitivity to her pain. He answered in no uncertain terms and left to get more dressing material. Then the Spirit of God began to speak to his heart. When he returned, a surprise awaited him. Before he had a chance to pull the drape aside to reenter the treatment area, he heard the patient and her family talking, praying for her, and for him. As he entered the treatment area, their eyes met, and tears came to his eyes. When he apologized, healing took place.

The Gospels present a Saviour who loved humanity and healed the sick in both body and soul. Christ calls upon modern disciples to do the same.

A THEOLOGY OF HEALTH AND HEALING

---

[1] I wish to thank Harvey Brenneise, Sandra White, and the reference and research staff of the James White Library of Andrews University for kindly doing a literature search for me on this topic and sending me copies of articles unavailable at my location.

[2] A leper (Matt. 8:1-4), a centurion's servant (verses 5-13), Simon's mother-in-law (verses 14, 15), two demoniacs (verses 28-34), a paralytic (Matt. 9:1-8), a woman with a hemorrhage and Jairus's daughter (verses 18-26), two blind men (verses 27-31), a demon-possessed blind and mute man (verses 22-24), a Canaanite woman's demon-possessed daughter (Matt. 15:21-28), a "moonstruck" boy (Matt. 17:14-21), and two blind men (Matt. 20:29-34). Matthew also records two miracles of providing bread to crowds (Matt. 14:15-21 and Matt. 15:32-38).

[3] Cf. Matt. 4:23, 24; 8:16, 17; 9:35-38; 11:2-6, 20-24; 12:15-21; 14:14, 34-36; 15:29-31; 19:1, 2; and 21:14-16.

[4] "Son of David" appears nine times in Matthew. Its Christological overtones are immediately emphasized at the commencement of the book by inclusion in the geneology of Jesus. None of the other Gospels has as many references to the "Son of David." The term "Lord" also carries Messianic significance and is used frequently when the people call upon Jesus for help. (cf. Matt. 8:2, 8, 25; 14:30; 15:22, 25; 20:31).

[5] See Matt. 9:27-31; 15:21-28; 17:14-20; 20:29-34.

[6] A man with an unclean spirit (Mark 1:21-28), the mother-in-law of Simon (verses 29-31), a leper (verses 40-45), a paralytic (Mark 2:1-12), a man with a withered hand (Mark 3:1-6), a demoniac (Mark 5:1-20), a woman with a hemorrhage and Jairus's daughter (verses 21-43), a Greek Syrophoenician woman's demon-possessed daughter (Mark 7:24-30), a deaf mute (verses 31-37), a blind man (Mark 8:22-26), a boy possessed by a mute spirit (Mark 9:14-29), and blind Bartimaeus (Mark 10:46-52). We find also two miracles of feeding—5,000 (Mark 6:35-52) and 4,000 (Mark 8:1-9). The summaries of Jesus' healing work appear in Mark 1:32-34, 39; 3:9-12; 6:54-56.

[7] The demoniac of the Gergesenes (Mark 5:1-5), the woman with the hemorrhage (verses 25, 26), and the demon-possessed boy (Mark 9:14-22).

[8] For a discussion of the Messianic secret, see James L. Blevins, *The Messianic Secret of Markan Research: 1901-1976* (Washington, D.C.: University Press of America, 1981); and Christopher Tuckett, ed., *The Messianic Secret,* Issues in Religion and Theology, No. 1 (Philadelphia: Fortress, 1983).

[9] The healing miracles involve a man with an unclean spirit (Luke 4:31-37), Simon's mother-in-law (verses 38, 39), a leper (Luke 5:12-16), a paralytic (verses 17-26), a man with a withered hand (Luke 6:6-11), a centurion's servant (Luke 7:1-10), the son of the widow of Nain (verses 11-17), a demoniac (Luke 8:26-39), Jairus's daughter and the woman with the hemorrage (verses 40-56), a boy with an evil spirit (Luke 9:37-43), a mute with a demon (Luke 11:14-16), a woman bent over for 18 years (Luke 13:10-17), a man with dropsy (Luke 14:1-6), 10 lepers (Luke 17:12-19), a blind man (Luke 18:35-43), and the high priest's servant (Luke 22:50, 51). We also find one feeding miracle of 5,000 (Luke 9:10-17). The summaries of Jesus' healing ministry occur in Luke 4:40, 41; 6:17-19; 7:18-23; 9:10, 11; 10:13-15; 13:31-33; 24:19-21.

[10] The son of a king's officer (John 4:46-54, a paralyzed man (John 5:2-15), a man born blind (John 9:1-41), and Lazarus (John 11:1-46). The book also records the miracle of feeding 5,000 (John 6:1-15) and two summaries of His healing ministry (verses 1-4; 20:30, 31).

[11] Cf. Sean Freyne, *Galilee, Jesus, and the Gospels: Literary Approaches and Historical Investigations* (Philadelphia: Fortress, 1988), pp. 232-239.

[12] See, for example, a tree and its fruits (Matt. 7:15-23), good and bad trees (Matt. 12:33-37), marriage and divorce (Matt. 19:3-12), the resurrection and marriage (Matt.

22:23-33), the great judgment (Matt. 25:31-46), marriage and divorce (Mark 10:2-12), the resurrection and marriage (Mark 12:18-27), the mouth speaks the abundance of the heart (Luke 6:43-45), the good Samaritan (Luke 10:25-37), the resurrection and marriage (Luke 20:27-40), the resurrection of Lazarus, the state of man in death (John 11:1-44), the believer and Christ united (John 15:1-16), and the believer and God (John 17:21-23).

[13] The four major expressions of the doctrine of the unity of man in the Scriptures are: man's nature (a union of the breath of life and the dust of the earth), marriage (the two become one), the bodily resurrection of the dead, and judgment by works.

[14] The terminology "righteousness by" is Pauline and does not appear in the Gospels. The closest approach to the Pauline terminology is Matt 12:37: "For by your words you will be acquitted, and by your words you will be condemned" (NIV).

[15] It is interesting that Matthew 25:31-46 refers to the saved as "the righteous." They are the sheep, the people of the King, and do what is right because of who they are. Their deeds express their inward reality.

[16] Of Matthew's 14 miracles, 11 have requests (spoken or implied). Exceptions include: Peter's mother-in-law (Matt. 8:14, 15), the Gergesene demoniacs (verses 28-34), and the man with the withered hand (Matt. 12:9-14). Of Mark's 13 miracles, 10 have requests. Exceptions include: a man with an unclean spirit (Mark 1:21-28), the man with the withered hand (Mark 3:1-6), and the Gergesene demoniac (Mark 5:1-20). Of Luke's 17 miracles, nine have requests. Exceptions include: a man with an unclean spirit (Luke 4:31-37), the man with the withered hand (Luke 6:6-11, the widow of Nain's son (Luke 7:11-17), the Gergesene demoniac (Luke 8:26-39), a mute man (Luke 11:14-16), a woman with a spirit of infirmity (Luke 13:10-17), a man with dropsy (Luke 14:1-6), and the high priest's servant (Luke 22:50, 51). Of John's four miracles, two have requests. Exceptions include the man at the Pool of Bethesda (John 5:2-15) and the man born blind (John 9:1-41).

[17] For a description of different models and understandings of health and sickness between various cultures, see John J. Pilch, "Sickness and Healing in Luke-Acts" in *The Social World of Luke-Acts: Models for Interpretations,* ed. Jerome H. Neyrey (Peabody, Mass.: Hendrickson, 1991), pp. 181-209.

Tom Shepherd teaches in the Religion Department at Union College, Lincoln, Nebraska.

Chapter 6

SIGNS AND WONDERS, POWER AND GLORY

James W. Zackrison, D.Miss.

The devil made me do it!" Sound familiar? Are demons an active force in today's world? Is there such a thing as demon possession? Are the biblical accounts of demon possession really only stories of unrecognized mental illnesses?

The advent of the Age of Aquarius and the New Age movement have given new life to the issue of the role of Satan and his cohorts in human affairs. Voodoo was voted as a national religious cult of an entire nation. During military interventions in a Caribbean nation United Nations personnel were astounded to see soldiers running toward them throwing "sacred dust" into the air, believing that the spirits used the dust to make them impervious to bullets. The entertainment industry highly regards channelers, the modern name for spirit mediums, and movie stars who win awards regularly credit their "spirit guides" for their success.[1] Few people realize the behind-the-scenes spiritistic worldviews that permeate the computer game and entertainment software industry, often run by those whom someone has called "leftover hippies" from the 1960s and 1970s counterculture movements.[2]

That's not all. Listen to this: "Much of *Cyberia* (a book about the contemporary counterculture) is given over to speculation about the eschatological zero hour, which is scheduled for sometime around the millennium."[3] Sound familiar? What's the worldview behind such a statement? The author terms it "techno-paganism." What does it believe? That "rationalism and intuition, materialism and mysticism, science and magic, are converging."

Followers of this philosophy conclude that the observer and the observed are one and the same thing, reality itself. It is another name for pantheism, the concept that everything is God and He is not a personal being. Underground chemists create mind-expanding "designer drugs" and, writes the same author, "decide what they'd like reality to be like, then—in a submolecular shamanic visionquest—compose a chemical that will alter their observation in a specific way."

Add to this the so-called Gaea hypothesis that the world is a living creature with a consciousness, the "earth goddess" who is becoming aware that people are not treating her well. One of these days, the hypothesis says, the "earth" will get tired of the whole thing and rebel, eliminating humanity as we know it. The same people believe that the membrane of computer networks being created over the surface of the earth may "come to life" and create havoc. Sound like science fiction? Maybe so, but believe it or not, some of the followers of this worldview are producing the computer games our children and grandchildren play every day and the "children's" cartoons seen on TV all the time. They have computer bulletin boards where they get together with names like "Deus et Machina" (god in the machine), "Quill and Inkpot," "Ritual Magik Online," and "BathoNet" (a pun on Bathomet, the satanic goat who presides during witches' sabbaths).[4]

And what is their justification for satanic activity? A Bible verse, Matthew 18:20: "For where two or three are gathered together in my name, there I am in the midst of them" (KJV). Want to guess who is really "in the midst of them"? Small wonder that some of the leading figures have taken names like Queen Mu, R. U. Sirius, and Merry Prankster, and call themselves "zippies," for "Zen-inspired pagan professional." They refer to low-level computer bulletin boards as "electronic familiars" and "demons" that they then name after so-called low-ranking demons. Beyond computer games, the same worldview extends into rock music and many other areas of contemporary society.

Satan manages to deceive people into doing things his way through three approaches. The first is to spiritualize all problems. The most common indication of this approach is "Let's pray about it." Honest prayer is always appropriate, but all too often the phrase means "Let's not do anything to solve the problem." A second error is the idea behind the reaction "The devil made me do it!" People who seriously believe this feel powerless to do anything about their condition. The third error is to deny in the name of science any supernatural intervention, and to consider all mental health problems to have purely biological or psychological origins.

BIBLICAL PERSPECTIVES ON MIRACLES

Before considering demon possession itself, we must look at the biblical perspective on miracles, divine intervention, and what the Bible calls "signs and wonders" (2 Cor. 12:12).[5]

The Greek word for miracles, *dunamis*, means inherent power, the power residing in something by virtue of its nature, or the power a person or thing exerts and puts forth. Wonders, *terata* in Greek, indicate the effect of the *dunamis* on the observers, almost always that of astonishment. Signs, *semeia* in Greek, refer to seals or verifications God uses to authenticate the persons through whom He works the miracles and wonders.[6] Thus Jesus' disciples affirmed: "This salvation, which was first announced by the Lord, was confirmed to us by those who heard him. God also testified to it by signs, wonders and various miracles, and gifts of the Holy Spirit distributed according to his will" (Heb. 2:3, 4).*

DO SIGNS AND WONDERS REALLY HAPPEN?

Signs and wonders are often so sensational and highly publicized that they frighten people, especially in the scientifically oriented Western world. Two things lend themselves to these perceptions. First, it's relatively easy to acknowledge signs and wonders as long as they happen at a physical distance from us personally. When they occur close to home, it's typical to be skeptical and reticent to acknowledge their validity.

Second, it's an almost spontaneous reaction to downplay miracles, signs, and wonders, because we can so easily confuse them with counterfeits. Paul himself warned: "The coming of the lawless one will be in accordance with the work of Satan displayed in all kinds of counterfeit miracles, signs and wonders, and in every sort of evil that deceives those who are perishing" (2 Thess. 2:9, 10). The existence of counterfeits, however, does not nullify the validity of the genuine.

"With Signs Following"

Miracles, signs, and wonders comprise a broad spectrum of events and activities promised to Jesus' followers in Mark's version of the Great Commission: "And these signs will accompany those who believe: In my name they will drive out demons; they will speak in new tongues; they will pick up snakes with their hands; and when they drink deadly poison, it will not hurt them at all; they will place their hands on sick people, and they will get well" (Mark 16:15-18).[7]

Power Encounters

This kind of confrontation is known as a "power encounter." The classic Old Testament example was Elijah's duel with the prophets of Baal on Mount Carmel (1 Kings 18). Others include Jesus' confrontation with a legion of demons in the cemetery in Gadara (Mark 5) and Paul's showdown with Elymas the sorcerer (Acts 13:6-12).

A review of the skirmishes between Nebuchadnezzar and Daniel illustrates how power encounters work. When Nebuchadnezzar, renowned king of Babylon, wrote to his subjects: "It is my pleasure to tell you about the miraculous signs and wonders that the Most High God has performed for me. How great are his signs, how mighty his wonders! His kingdom is an eternal kingdom; his dominion endures from generation to generation" (Dan. 4:2, 3), he was talking from personal experience. An absolute monarch with the power of life and death in his hands, Nebuchadnezzar had no national assembly to question his commands, wishes, or desires; no checks and balances on anything he did. An accomplished builder, he could truthfully say (though too arrogantly), "Is not this the great Babylon I have built as the royal residence, by my mighty power and for the glory of my majesty?" (verse 30).

Behind all this pomp and circumstance, however, lay a series of encounters that eventually led Nebuchadnezzar to acknowledge a greater Power. Again and again that Power beat him at his own game. Hostages from a conquered land became his main advisors; dreams were interpreted and came true to the letter; uncompromising servants of the God of Israel wouldn't burn in the hottest of flames; and Daniel himself informed the king of a coming bout with madness. It took only one heavenly messenger, or "watcher," as the King James Version puts it, to fulfill that prediction and reduce Nebuchadnezzar to the status of an animal! Signs and wonders became the evidence he needed to cross the line and take a stand on the side of the God of heaven.[8]

Do Miracles Still Happen?

Do these things happen today, or are they confined to ancient historical records and missionary stories from too far away for verification? Are they usually just counterfeits playing tricks with the nervous system?

Counterfeits always exist in the form of quacks, charlatans, and sensationalist faith healers. They blow on people and supposedly cause them to be slain in the Spirit, hit people in the head and ask if they see lights (who wouldn't?), and call these actions the "wonders" referred to in the Bible.

Counterfeits, however, don't negate the genuine. They make us cautious, but not so hesitant that we turn off the power of God. As C. S. Lewis observes: "God does not shake miracles into Nature at random . . . they come on great occasions; they are found at the great ganglions of history. . . . If your life does not happen to be near one of those great ganglions, how should you expect to see one?"[9]

Signs and wonders are part of a larger picture we call the "great controversy," the entire picture of eschatology from the time of Jesus until the Second Coming. Within that time span the Lord works through the power of the Holy Spirit to unchain human minds and reorient them toward the kingdom of God. Jesus "disarmed the powers and authorities, [and] made a public spectacle of them, triumphing over them at the cross" (Col. 2:15). That victory, however, while final in the long run, was not the end of the war. Satan continues to blind people's spiritual eyes (2 Cor.

4:4), block spiritual discernment (1 Cor. 2:14), cause them to see evil as good (Rom. 1:25), and distort spiritual discernment with false doctrines (Rev. 14:8). Most of the time, God uses solid biblical teaching in the form of Bible studies, classes, study groups, and sermons as His vehicle to reverse the situation (Rom. 10:17). When the circumstances call for it, however, the Lord works through His people in marked, visible manifestations that we call signs and wonders.[10]

Stories of the miraculous fill the Bible.[11] Children are born to barren parents, vast numbers of people cross bodies of water that dry up before their eyes, a huge fish swallows a reluctant prophet and later regurgitates him at a designated geographical location. The blind see, people with incurable disease are healed, a small boy's lunch pail supplies thousands, and even the dead live again.

The early church understood miracles to confirm the validity of the message they taught (Acts 2:22), and the resurrection of Jesus, an astounding miracle verified by both believers and non-believers, became the centerpiece of apostolic preaching (Acts 17:31). Missionary history and contemporary church life is also replete with the stories of miracles.

A GENERAL CATEGORY

"Miracles" is a general category for the kinds of signs and wonders we have considered so far. The basic purpose of miracles is to awaken and strengthen faith in God. "They focus attention on the real source of all that is good in the world; they remind us that God is indeed alive and well."[12]

DIVINE HEALING

Scripture and religious writings often mention divine healing, usually as a direct answer to prayer. The following story offers a typical modern example. A 30-year-old woman diagnosed with colon cancer learned that she had only two months to live. She was prayed for and anointed on a Sabbath afternoon. Three days later her doctor, an atheist, told her, "You must serve a very powerful God!" because he couldn't find any trace of the cancer.[13]

The sensationalist activity of self-styled faith healers, witch doctors, shamans, etc., does not discount the validity of miraculous healings through prayer. The popularity of these aberrations, however, make instances of the true gift of miraculous healing less frequent.

The Bible uses the plural "healings" (1 Cor. 12:28, KJV), possibly referring to the healing of emotional and spiritual illnesses as well as physical healing. Divine healing does not give a person supernatural power over diseases. It doesn't make doctors and nurses obsolete. Nor are healings always permanent. As far as we know, even the people Jesus healed eventually died. Paul had a "thorn in the flesh" (2 Cor. 12:7-9) that the Lord chose not to remove. Paul recommended a natural remedy for Timothy's stomach problem rather than handing him a "sacred handkerchief," something used earlier with great effect in Ephesus (Acts 19:12).

Following this lead, Ellen White often connects this kind of healing with medical missionary work. "God's miracles do not always bear the outward semblance of miracles. Often they are brought about in a way which looks like the natural course of events. When we pray for the sick, we also work for them. We answer our own prayers by using the remedies within our reach" (*The Seventh-day Adventist Bible Commentary,* Ellen G. White Comments, vol. 7, p. 938).

In summary, Scripture does not specifically define how God handles disease and illness, and those assigned the gift of healing do not manipulate God. They are simply instruments in His hands for Him to use in times and places He sees fit.

CASTING OUT DEMONS

Casting out devils is a form of power encounter. Few events are as spectacular as this one. The Bible contains numerous stories of deliverance. Some contemporary people, however, claim to assign "demons" to every malady of human nature, from headaches to family infighting. Such a view has little biblical evidence to support it.

On the other hand, the closer we approach the Second Coming, as God withdraws His Spirit from the earth, the more opportunity Satan has to work openly. If divine healing is not used judiciously and under careful control, it can easily be counterfeited by Satan himself and turned into an apparent victory for him rather than for the Lord (see Mark 9:14-29).[14]

INTERCESSION AND INTERCESSORY PRAYER

Intercessory prayer is a type of prayer focused on a particular issue. Experience demonstrates that every church has someone with this gift. It is one of the most powerful gifts a congregation can have. An intercessory prayer ministry will produce miracles, both spectacular and "quiet." It will transform the ministry and growth of your church.

SUMMARY

Demonic activity in today's world is no less apparent than in the time of Jesus. Satan is not asleep by any means. All kinds of factors affect mental health, and the problem is often treatable by established means of counseling, therapy, and medical intervention. At times, however, Satan manages to take over a person's life to the point that demon possession enters the picture. This is just as real today as it ever was, and the Christian church and its medical facilities need to be prepared to face it.

---

*Bible references in this chapter are from the New International Version unless noted otherwise.

---

[1] For an inside look at the New Age movement from an Adventist perspective, see Will Barron, *Deceived by the New Age* (Boise, Idaho: Pacific Press Pub. Assn., 1990).

[2] For a look at the inside of this counterculture, see Mark Dery, *Escape Velocity: Cyberculture at the End of the Century* (New York: Grove Press, 1996).

[3] *Ibid.,* p. 41.

[4] *Ibid.,* p. 56.

[5] The phrase "signs and wonders" first appears in a letter from Nebuchadnezzar, king of Babylon, to his subjects (Dan. 4) and reappears in Peter's sermon on the day of Pentecost (Acts 2:22). The purpose of signs and wonders is to confirm to unbelievers and skeptical believers that God is indeed working in a marked way in a particular circumstance.

[6] Orton Wiley, *Christian Theology* (Kanasa City: Beacon Hill Press, 1950), vol. 1, p. 151.

[7] Scholars have some question about the authenticity of these verses. See Donald Guthrie, *New Testament Introduction,* revised edition (Downers Grove, Ill.: InterVarsity Press, 1990), pp. 89-93, for a summary of the debate. *The Seventh-day Adventist Bible Commentary* is of the opinion that textual evidence favors the inclusion of these verses (vol. 5, p. 658). Ellen White cites the verses as authoritative scripture *(The Kress Collection,* p. 126).

[8] "King Nebuchadnezzar, before whom Daniel so often honored the name of God, was finally thoroughly converted, and learned to 'praise and extol and honor the King of heaven'" (Ellen White, in *Review and Herald,* Jan. 11, 1906).

SIGNS AND WONDERS, POWER AND GLORY

[9] C. S. Lewis, *Miracles: A Preliminary Study* (New York: Macmillan Co., 1947), pp. 167, 168.

[10] For a contemporary evaluation of spiritual warfare and the various points of view involved, see Thomas H. McAlpine, *Facing the Powers* (Monrovia, Calif.: MARC, 1991) and John White, *When the Spirit Comes With Power* (Downers Grove, Ill.: InterVarsity Press, 1988). For two theological analyses see Merrill F. Unger, *Demons in the World Today* (Wheaton, Ill.: Tyndale House Publishers, Inc., 1971) and Donald Grey Barnhouse, *The Invisible War* (Grand Rapids: Zondervan Publishing House, 1965). For a cautious evaluation, see Thomas Ice and Robert Dean, Jr., *Overrun by Demons* (Eugene, Oreg.: Harvest House Publishers, 1990). See ed. Murthy, *The Handbook of Spiritual Warfare* (Nashville: Thomas Nelson Publishers, 1992) for an encyclopedic source of information.

[11] Lewis's *Miracles* is a good general treatise on miracles.

[12] Richard Rice, *The Reign of God* (Berrien Springs, Mich.: Andrews University Press, 1985), p. 83.

[13] Reported by Rich DuBose in *FYE,* the North American Division information newsletter, Dec. 11, 1995.

[14] For more information on devil possession and the gift of exorcism, see *The Seventh-day Adventist Bible Commentary,* volume 5, pages 575-577, and *The Great Controversy,* chapter 31. Outbreaks of so-called deliverance ministries in the Adventist Church have gone far beyond the bounds of biblical guidelines. For more information, you can obtain a number of documents from the General Conference Biblical Research Institute on this subject.

James Zackrison is the director of the Sabbath School/Personal Ministries Department of the General Conference of Seventh-day Adventists, Silver Spring, Maryland.

Chapter 7

THE SABBATH IS GOOD NEWS

James W. Zackrison, D.Miss.

The Sabbath is good news for many reasons. While we Seventh-day Adventists have a great interest in proving that the Sabbath is the seventh day of the week, there is more to it than that. The Sabbath also has deep spiritual meanings. Notice how Scripture describes the finished creation: "God saw all that he had made, and it was very good. And there was evening, and there was morning—the sixth day" (Gen. 1:31).* The Sabbath is good news because it shows that God does not do things halfway. We can trust Him to do it right.

Genesis 1:27, 28 informs us that God created humanity in His image. Thus the Sabbath is good news because it gives us a firm handle to hang on to regarding our beginnings as human beings.

Genesis 2:15 says that "the Lord God took the man and put him in the Garden of Eden to work it and take care of it." The Sabbath is good news because it gives us a firm anchor to life's meaning. Life is rooted in God and His creation, and the Sabbath reminds us of that fact on a weekly basis.

Psalm 92, a psalm for the Sabbath day, asks us to praise the Lord in the morning and in the evening, to make music, and to be glad for His mighty deeds. It tells us that the wicked will not prosper, but will meet their ultimate fate, while the righteous "will flourish like a palm tree, they will grow like a cedar of Lebanon; planted in the house of the Lord, they will flourish in the courts of our God. They will still bear fruit in old age, they will stay fresh and green" (verses 12-14). The Sabbath is good news because it gives us something concrete to worship, pointing us to a God who can be trusted.

Psalm 96, celebrating the joy and enthusiasm of true worship, urges us to proclaim the name of the Lord among the nations, to declare His marvelous deeds because He is worthy of praise, having made the heavens. Because He reigns, "the world is firmly established, it cannot be moved; he will judge the peoples with equity" (verse 10). The Sabbath is good news because it creates, according to Abraham Heschel, a cathedral in time.[1] Having a fixed time to worship regardless of where a person may be or live in the world is good news because it tells us whom to praise and brings us together into His presence. We have no need to wonder whom or when to worship.

Mark 2:27 declares that the Sabbath was made for human benefit. It is good news because it offers an opportunity to look at the world through the window of eternity—to recapture Eden once a week.

Isaiah 58:14 announces that those who keep the Sabbath will "ride on the heights of the land" and "feast on the inheritance of your father Jacob." The Sabbath is good news because it gives us something definite to be loyal to amid the conflicting demands for loyalty we encounter in everyday life.

Isaiah 58:13 says that the Sabbath is a particular day. The Sabbath is good news because it is God's distinctive insignia. The number seven is unrelated to any other time sequence in nature. It eliminates the worship of astrology, idols, or any form of nature. Again in the words of Abraham Heschel, "the Sabbath teaches all beings whom to praise."[2]

THE SABBATH—A BRIGHT SPOT IN A DARK WORLD

God was obliged to put a limit on time, because humanity tried to become like Him in the wrong ways. They forgot that God is the Creator and that they are only a part of His universal creation. The Sabbath is a bright spot in an otherwise dark world because it gives us an incentive to remember what reality was like originally and what it will be like again in the future.

WHY GOD LIMITED TIME

Only the human race lives in time as we know it. God lives in eternity, a state that has neither beginning nor end. We humans cannot fully comprehend eternity, because we have both a beginning and an end. The Sabbath focuses our minds once a week on the spiritual realities of eternity. It is a time-bound symbol of the relationship God wants to have with born-again humans. As it was timeless before the Fall, so someday we will be released from its time-binding, and it will become an eternal symbol of a restored relationship.

Adam and Eve's fall created a separation between the human race and God. It is easy for us to talk in terms of death and degradation, because they are tangible. But it is more difficult to think in terms of separation, because separation from God is an intangible spiritual reality. Nevertheless, that is what happened. Sin broke the bond between Creator and human creation.

According to Exodus 20:11, "in six days the Lord made the heavens and the earth, the sea, and all that is in them, but he rested on the seventh day. Therefore the Lord blessed the Sabbath day and made it holy." The Sabbath takes the mind back to the original and off the current situation. Conflicting ideas about the origin of the human race inevitably focus on humanity itself. The Sabbath, reflecting on the original, directs the mind to God.

Deuteronomy 5:15 reads: "Remember that you were slaves in Egypt and that the Lord your God brought you out of there with a mighty hand and an outstretched arm. *Therefore* the Lord your God has commanded you to observe the Sabbath day." The word "therefore" indicates that the Sabbath has a special significance because it is a reminder of the *solution* to the sin problem. We are no different from the Israelites in that respect. We too need reminders of the "mighty and outstretched arm" of God.

Ezekiel 20:12 and 20 tell us that the Sabbath has a special meaning because it shows whom we can trust and in whom we can place our eternal confidence. The very fact that most people do *not* keep the Sabbath emphasizes the trust placed in God by those who do observe it. That is why Mark 2:28 points out that the Sabbath was "made for man, not man for the Sabbath."

The experience of a Sabbath confrontation with Satan recorded in Mark 1:21-28 demonstrates that God is in ultimate charge of everything. Satan cannot stand up to God when it comes to an encounter. We humans are the beneficiaries of that power. A healing on the Sabbath recounted in Luke 6:6-11 shows again that the Sabbath exists for the benefit of the human race. Jesus restores a shriveled hand. Would that man ever forget the Sabbath?

The Sabbath Is a Sign of a Restored Kingdom

The apostle John, who wrote some 30 years later than the other New Testament writers, explains that Jesus is the light of the world, "the light that gives light to every man" (John 1:9). Jesus, the light, has broken into the gloom of human history. He has penetrated the darkness of sin to bring eternal life now to those who will let His light shine into their hearts.

The Sabbath becomes the weekly reminder that Jesus breaks into the darkness. The world, Abraham Heschel reminds us, was created in six days, but it was a world without a soul. It is the Sabbath that gives it its soul.[3] Nearly all religions have a holy place, but before God ever established a holy place, He established a holy *time*. This is unique in religious history. That is the real intention behind God's blessing of the Sabbath day. Again quoting Abraham Heschel, "The light of a man's face during the week is not the same as it is on the Sabbath."[4]

The Sign of a Restored Relationship

Isaiah 58:12 outlines the bond between the Sabbath and the believers' relationship to God: "Your people will rebuild the ancient ruins and will raise up the age-old foundations; you will be called Repairer of Broken Walls, Restorer of Streets with Dwellings." The concept of rebuilding ancient ruins and raising up age-old foundations is the Bible's way of saying that the followers of the Lord are pointing people back to God's plan. To be a restorer of the streets is to place people on the right road that will take them to the heavenly city.

In verse 13 Isaiah points out five things that apply to the restoration of the spirit of the Sabbath in people's minds:

1. Keeping the Sabbath.
2. Not doing your own pleasure.

3. Calling the Sabbath a delight.
4. Honor it by not going "your own way."
5. Not speaking idle words.

As a result of faithfulness to the Sabbath, God's people will find their joy in the Lord, will ride on the heights of the land, and will feast on the believers' inheritance, confirmed by the Lord Himself, because "the mouth of the Lord has spoken" (verse 14).

The Sabbath Will Always Be There

The Sabbath is part of the structure of the universe itself. God put it there because He knew it benefited created beings. Because it is an integral part of the universe, it will exist throughout eternity.

Hebrews 4 is an often overlooked chapter on the Sabbath. It uses the Sabbath as a symbol of eternal "rest"—salvation. The common symbol for this rest in the New Testament is the phrase "the lamb of God." The writer of Hebrews, however, chooses a symbol that we already participate in once a week: "for anyone who enters God's rest also rests from his own work, just as God did from his" (Heb. 4:10). Here is one of the best texts in the Bible to explain the real essence of the Sabbath. It is a call to trust God—to follow His example. The Sabbath is not a "work," but a matter of trusting God. The logical conclusion is that entering God's rest is the best thing to do. We have to make that decision if we intend to inherit the New Earth.

The Sabbath, then, is important in the judgment. Adventist pioneer Joseph Bates's original contribution to the concept of the Sabbath, based on Revelation 14:12, was that it was a symbol of a restored relationship and a recognition of Jesus as Lord. Out of this understanding grew the concept of the seal of God as it relates to the Sabbath.[5] The following chart puts the picture together.

A Cathedral in Time—The Meaning of the Sabbath

	Genesis 1-3 "In the beginning"	John 1 "In the beginning"	Heb. 1:2; 4:1-4 "In these last days"	Rev. 14:6-12 "Eternal gospel"
Creation Account	God created	All things were made by the Word	Spoken by His Son, who made all things	Give glory to God, who made the world
Result	Sabbath established	Restoration from the Fall	The Sabbath "rest" a symbol of eternal life	The Sabbath a sign of loyalty
Time	Creation of time in eternity	Eternal time returns	The experience of eternal time	Eternal time recognized

THE SABBATH AND HEALTH

Healing has many facets. The Sabbath rest is significant from a personal health perspective as well as a spiritual one. Stress brings on physical and mental disorders. The participants in a 1993 symposium of health futurists from around the world predicted what they believed would be the diseases of the next decade. They asserted that there would be a great increase in diseases of the immune system and behavior-related diseases because of increased fear and the fracturing of families.

The Sabbath is health-related, because it gives opportunity to escape from the everyday world and enter into "God's rest" through worship, new paths of thought, and a general relaxation from the cares of this life. The Sabbath rest is one of the ways that Jesus' words in Matthew 11:28, 29 become reality: "Come to me, all you who are weary and burdened, and I will give you rest. Take my yoke upon you and learn from me, for I am gentle and humble in heart, and you will find rest for your souls."

Getting together for worship on Sabbath is good for health. We may view the congregation as God's divinely appointed support group. Statistical data shows that the relationship between social isolation and early death is as strong as the relationship between dying and smoking or high levels of cholesterol. From a statistical standpoint, the data suggests that it may be as important for your health to be socially integrated as it is to stop smoking or to reduce a high cholesterol level. Going to church on Sabbath is more than a duty—it's also good for your health!

Healing on the Sabbath

In keeping with His statement in Mark 2:28 that the "Sabbath was made for man," Jesus performed a significant number of miracles on that day. Most of His Sabbath miracles occurred in the presence of the popular religious leaders both as evidences of His divinity and to demonstrate proper Sabbath observance. The beneficiaries of these miracles, however, were the people He healed.

The religious leaders of the time had their own ideas about why people got sick in the first place, and especially about healing on the Sabbath. They were concerned about making a clear distinction at what point an activity became "work." Any activity was legitimate on the Sabbath until it turned into "work." Their numerous rules of Sabbath observance were the guidelines by which one could determine the point of transition to "work."

The rules the Pharisees devised for Sabbath healing seemed to have a clear-cut logic. They determined that if a person was in a life-threatening situation, you could seek to prevent the loss of life, but they opposed the promotion of healing. In other words, if your hand or wrist were cut and bleeding, you could stop the bleeding, because it was a threat to life. But you could not put salve on the wound to promote healing! The moment the body began to heal, it converted to "work," and therefore the activity was not compatible with Sabbathkeeping. What is wrong with this logic? The problem is that it sees humanity as made for the Sabbath instead of the Sabbath made for humanity. It is what made Jesus angry with the Pharisees (Mark 3:5).

I remember a question I once missed on a driving test: "If you are stopped at a red light, and a police officer signals you to go ahead, whom do you obey, the officer or the red light?" Why I answered "the red light," I don't know. The examiner commented, "Since when do you obey a machine instead of a human being?" The Pharisees were doing something similar with the Sabbath. It was almost a mechanical thing rather than a spiritual experience. God saw no incompatability between true Sabbath observance and healing the man with the withered hand. The idea that the body was "working" if it did any "healing" on the Sabbath was a purely arbitrary position. The religious teachers probably conceived it with all good intentions, but it soon degenerated into a mechanical Sabbath observance that took the joy and the meaning out of the day.

To Heal or Not to Heal?

That is the question for the contemporary world. The general answer is that we should limit normal work as much as possible on the Sabbath, but that indispensable things have to go on. Jesus healed emergency cases, or cases He came across because He happened to be where the sick people surfaced. He wasn't a doctor, nor did He work in the medical profession. On the other hand, no one would have been disturbed by what He did on Sabbath had it not been for the self-generated rules imposed by the Pharisees. Exactly what to do and not do in an Adventist medical institution on Sabbath is a judgment call that has to be made by the people involved, who know what the circumstances dictate. The same is true for Adventist firefighters, military personnel, or any of a multitude of other professions and vocations. Ellen White writes: "God could not for a moment stay His hand, or man would faint and die. And man also has a work to perform on this day. The necessities of life must be attended to, the sick must be cared for, the wants of the needy must be supplied. He will not be held guiltless who neglects to relieve suffering on the Sabbath. God's holy rest day was made for man, and acts of mercy are in perfect harmony with its intent. God does not desire His creatures to suffer an hour's pain that may be relieved upon the Sabbath or any other day" (*The Desire of Ages,* p. 207).

The other side of the coin is that we can take even legitimate activities too far. Keeping the Sabbath holy is not an option to be taken lightly. It is all too easy to excuse any specific activity for a lot of reasons, when in reality the motivation behind the attempt may be just a way of getting around what is right.

Abraham Heschel sums up the meaning of the Sabbath: "We usually think that the earth is our mother, that time is money and profit our mate. The seventh day is a reminder that God is our father, that time is life and the spirit our mate."[6] The Sabbath is indeed good news.

---

*Bible references in this chapter are from the New International Version.

---

[1] See Abraham Joshua Heschel, *The Sabbath: Its Meaning for Modern Man* (New York: Farrar, Straus and Giroux, 1951), p. 8

[2] *Ibid.,* p. 24.

[3] *Ibid.,* p. 83.

[4] *Ibid.,* p. 87.

[5] For more information on this point see C. Mervyn Maxwell, "Joseph Bates and Seventh-day Adventist Sabbath Theology," in *The Sabbath in Scripture and History* (Review and Herald Pub. Assn., 1982), pp. 352-363.

[6] Heschel, p. 76.

James Zackrison is the director of the Sabbath School/Personal Ministries Department of the General Conference of Seventh-day Adventists, Silver Spring, Maryland.

Chapter 8

"I THINK I'LL DOCTOR MYSELF"

Warren R. Peters, M.D., F.A.C.S.

How did the Seventh-day Adventist Church become health-conscious? What did Ellen White recommend about drugs, hydrotherapy, and healing remedies? Is there a difference between "natural" remedies and the medicines used by the medical profession? These are some of the questions we will take up in this chapter as we trace the history of the development of the use of natural remedies among Seventh-day Adventists.

A BRIEF HISTORY OF HEALTH IN THE BIBLE

As the nation of Israel emerged from a sea of polytheistic religions and cultures, God presented to them a style of living that included sanitation, disease prevention, and a diet interwoven with spiritual lessons: "If you listen carefully to the voice of the Lord your God and do what is right in his eyes, if you pay attention to his commands and keep all his decrees, I will not bring on you any of the diseases I brought on the Egyptians, for I am the Lord, who heals you" (Ex. 15:26, NIV).

During the first few years after Christ's death His followers continued to blend physical and spiritual well-being into their teachings. Soon, however, the church began to distort the message of wholeness. They often taught that physical abuse and withdrawing from society earned piety. The Mosaic and Christian teachings of humanity's wholeness got lost or disregarded. During the Dark Ages millions of people died when epidemics of cholera, plague, and dysentery swept across Europe and elsewhere. It was all unnecessary, because God had given rules of hygiene that would have prevented such carnage.

NEW EMPHASIS ON HEALTH

It was not until the late nineteenth century that people realized the connection between the spiritual life and physical well-being. Sylvester Graham, a Presbyterian minister, began to teach that avoiding alcohol and tobacco along with the use of unrefined flour was a moral obligation.[1] The founders of Oberlin College vowed: "That we may have time and health for the Lord's service, we will eat only plain and wholesome food, renouncing all bad habits, and especially the smoking and chewing of tobacco, unless it is necessary as a medicine, and deny ourselves all the strong and unnecessary drinks, even tea and coffee, as far as practicable, and everything expensive that is simply calculated to gratify appetite."[2] The Seventh-day Adventist movement emerged into this setting.

Are natural remedies a lost art, outdated relics from another era? Not at all. Today scientists are documenting the interaction of the mind and the body, and proclaiming the interrelatedness of spirit and body. The world has focused favorably on the "Adventist lifestyle."

NATURAL REMEDIES: ELLEN WHITE'S DEFINITION

Ellen White wrote and taught that mental, physical, and spiritual remedies affect the whole body. By her definition, natural remedies were predominately a style of living that helped health reformers avoid disease. Her most inclusive statement appeared in 1885: "There are many ways of practicing the healing art, but there is only one way that Heaven approves. God's remedies are the simple agencies of nature that will not tax or debilitate the system through their powerful properties. Pure air and water, cleanliness, a proper diet, purity of life, and a firm trust in God are remedies for the want of which thousands are dying; yet these remedies are going out of date because their skillful use requires work that the people do not appreciate. Fresh air, exercise, pure water, and clean, sweet premises are within the reach of all with but little expense; but drugs are expensive, both in the outlay of means and in the effect produced upon the system" (*Testimonies for the Church,* vol. 5, p. 443).

She wrote her first published treatise on health in 1864. It appears in *Spiritual Gifts,* book 4. Her topics ranged widely from dietary issues to substance abuse. We will review its contents as the basis of her understanding of the expression "natural remedies."

Ellen White contrasted natural and simple remedies for health to the heavy drugging practice of her day. She advocated personal hygiene, admonishing people to bathe daily with at least a sponge bath. Fresh air was to fill the sleeping rooms, and people needed to allow sunlight into the house by cutting or trimming away trees and shrubbery too close to the dwelling. Today's environmental building codes now require a prescribed number of air exchanges per hour for all buildings, so we may wonder why she stressed this. In the mid-1800s the culturally sophisticated did not want air and sunlight in their homes. They feared both because of the prevalence of malaria, thought to be carried by "night air."

Ellen White prescribed water as a remedy for sickness, even though many medical practitioners of that era treated fevers by dehydration through purging and abstinence from liquids. Nux vomica (strychnine), opium, mercury, calomel, and quinine—popular medicines of the time—she called "slow poisons." The physicians who heavily prescribed strong drugs and the sick themselves received strong words. "Physicians are censurable, but they are not the only ones at fault. The sick themselves, if they would be patient, diet and suffer a little, and give nature time to rally, would recover much sooner without the use of any medicine. Nature alone possesses curative powers. Medicines have no power to cure, but will most generally hinder nature in her efforts" (*Spiritual Gifts,* vol. 4, p. 136).

Seventh-day Adventists are proud of the fact that the modern medical community gives scientific credence to such natural remedies. Today even vegetarianism has a semblance of respectability. Science is demonstrating the benefits of the antioxidants in the deep-green and yellow vegetables. Animal foods have saturated fats and cholesterol linked with coronary artery disease and millions of deaths each year.

THE MASTER'S HEALING TOUCH

What do we Adventists do today with the very specific admonitions Ellen White made to use simple therapeutics? Can we be proud of this part of the health message, or is it a blight? What are some of the remedies she advocated?

Charcoal. Ellen White recommended charcoal to relieve some problems. "I have ordered the same treatment [charcoal poultices] for others who were suffering great pain, and it has brought relief and been the means of saving life. My mother had told me that snake bites and the sting of reptiles and poisonous insects could often be rendered harmless by the use of charcoal poultices" (*Selected Messages,* book 2, p. 245). She also said charcoal "is good for bloody dysentery and malaria, infected insect bite, great pain, fever, some forms of indigestion, bruised and inflamed hands from work injuries, severe inflammation of the eyes" (*ibid.,* pp. 294, 295, 298-300).[3]

We currently call this type of medical treatment acute care.[4] They are emergency room cases today, with some probably being hospitalized for intravenous rehydration and massive infusions of antibiotics. Every emergency room stocks powdered charcoal. It is the treatment of choice for acute poison or drug overdose problems.[5] The most highly adsorptive compound known, it is cheap, safe, and effective. It even lowers cholesterol.[6] Used internally, it relieves intestinal gas.

Herbs. We do not find much specific counsel on herbal therapy in Ellen White's writings, probably because of what was going on at the time in the medical profession itself. Herbalism was in turmoil in her day, as it is today. It is a quagmire of a few valuable, simple, tested, and proven therapeutics mixed with a mass of spurious and spiritualistic concoctions.

We have divided Ellen White's use of herbs into two categories: beverage and medicinal preparations. She brewed red clover flowers into a tea that took the place of regular tea and coffee as a hot beverage (see *Selected Messages,* book 2, p. 302). The second usage came in the form of therapeutics for specific ailments. For the treatment of nausea and seasickness, Ellen White recommended tea (black or green) or coffee (*ibid.*). Other recommendations were hop tea for insomnia, and catnip herbal tea for nervousness *(ibid.,* p. 297). Ellen White emphasized lifestyle measures first and foremost and safe, simple remedies as secondary therapies. "God's servants," she wrote, "should not administer medicines which they know will leave behind injurious effects upon the system, even if they do relieve present suffering. Every poisonous preparation in the vegetable and mineral kingdoms, taken into the system, will leave its wretched influence, affecting the liver and lungs, and deranging the system generally" *(Spiritual Gifts,* vol. 4, p. 140).

Varro E. Tyler, an herbalist, writes, "True herbalism encompasses scientific testing, honest reporting of the results, and safe use of effective herbs by informed practitioners and the public. It also includes the production and ethical marketing of herbal products. True herbalism brings honor to the wonder-filled world of plants. However, there is a dark side to herbalism which I call paraherbalism. The danger is ever-present that the good of herbalism will be destroyed by the evils of paraherbalism. That would be tragic because herbalism can play a useful role in the health-care arena."[7]

Hydrotherapy. Many Seventh-day Adventists remember hydrotherapy as a symbol of natural remedies in general. Something about this therapy bespeaks the comforts and the personal touch of "real" medical missionary work. It got its start with Vincent Priessnitz. Born in 1799 on a small farm in the mountains of Silesia, he noted that his sprained wrist improved quickly when he wrapped it in cold water bandages. He even cured his father's fevered cow with water applications. Though untrained in any formal system, he was the first to systematize the water treatments of those practitioners before him. In 1826 he founded the Water University of Gräfenberg in Silesia. The rural and quiet atmosphere of his institution accounted for some of his success. Patients escaped the general stresses of everyday life to a caring environment. By 1840 he was seeing 1,500 to 1,700 patients each year.[8] His theory of cure may not have been scientific, but he launched a method of healing that contrasted with the harsher practices of his day.[9]

When God gave Ellen White a vision of health that included the use of water, it was within a rich heritage of American health reform. An American, Joel Shew, visited Priessnitz at least twice during the 1840s to study the Europeans' methods and reform ideas. Shew added friction and massage to the hydrotherapy methods and founded the *Water Cure Journal* in New York in the 1840s. His colleague, R. T. Trall, joined him and opened a water cure center in New York City.

James C. Jackson was another physician who contributed to the water and health reform movement in America. Jackson had been a physician for several years, and brought the maturity and stability that gave the Dansville project one of the longest lives (100 years) of any of the health reform facilities. Dr. Jackson heavily influenced Ellen and James White. They traveled and lectured with him as they furthered the reform movement of the mid-nineteenth century. It was Dr. Jackson who gave specific substance to the health movement of the Seventh-day Adventist Church.

"Self-doctoring" was another part of the water cure philosophy and found a responsive fiber in American mentality. The lack of professional medical care for rural Americans caught up in the western migration and for the urban poor flowing in from Europe created a need for self-doctoring, what we often call today "medical missionary work."

Ellen White also stressed the theme of the physician as an educator. Speaking to physicians, she wrote, "God's blessing will rest upon every effort made to awaken an interest in health reform; for it is needed everywhere. There must be a revival on this subject; for God purposes to accomplish much through this agency. Present temperance with all its advantages in reference to health. Educate people in the laws of life so that they may know how to preserve health. The efforts actually put forth at present are not meeting the mind of God. Drug medication is a curse to this enlightened age. Educate away from drugs. Use them less and less, and depend more upon hygienic agencies; then nature will respond to God's physicians—pure air, pure water, proper exercise, a clear conscience" (*Medical Ministry,* p. 259).

ELLEN WHITE AND THE CUTTING EDGE OF REFORM

While currently no national organization of hydropathic

(water cure) healing exists, we do have a Seventh-day Adventist network of health-care facilities and practitioners that span the world. What made the difference? The Adventist system emerged from the hydropathic reform movement. It supports the same avoidance of drug treatments and the same emphasis on vegetarianism, fresh air, sunlight, moral uprightness, and search for individual perfection. Why is it alive while hydropathy is dead?

From water treatments to operating rooms. In vision Ellen White saw the need for training doctors and nurses in emerging health fields. She witnessed angels standing in the operating rooms, guiding the hands of God-fearing surgeons. "It is our privilege to use every God-appointed means in correspondence with our faith, and then trust in God, when we have urged the promise. If there is need of a surgical operation, and the physician is willing to undertake the case, it is not a denial of faith to have the operation performed" (*Selected Messages,* book 2, p. 284). What did God have in mind when He prompted Ellen White to join the hydropathic healers and condemn the use of drugs? Where is the consistency that allows Jesus to stand beside the surgeon and actually guide the surgical hand as it operates on the patient's anesthetized body? The answer lies in understanding what drugs are.

What is a "drug"? The appalling drugging practices of the nineteenth century deserved condemnation. Medical practitioners had very little if any formal education. Is it any wonder Ellen White would write, "Mercury, calomel, and quinine have brought their amount of wretchedness, which the day of God alone will fully reveal. Preparations of mercury and calomel taken into the system ever retain their poisonous strength as long as there is a particle of it left in the system. These poisonous preparations have destroyed their millions, and left sufferers upon the earth to linger out a miserable existence. . . . They are victims of poisonous preparations, which have been, in many cases, administered to cure some slight indisposition, which after a day or two of fasting would have disappeared without medicine" (*Spiritual Gifts,* vol. 4, p. 139). With this insight into the state of the drugging practices and her perception of the need for a deeper understanding of health and physiology, it is clear why Ellen White gave such a clarion call for reform and the admonition to avoid drugs that do not cure.

Quinine, an example. Allopathic practitioners frequently used quinine for any and every symptom. They prescribed large doses for simple fevers caused by upper respiratory infections as well as for malaria and other infectious diseases. Ellen White called for reform in its usage. Her recommendations regarding quinine give us a valuable perspective on her counsels regarding the use of drugs in general. She equated quinine with opium, strychnine, mercury, and other poisons. No one knew that mosquitoes carried malaria, but one of its symptoms was fever, and it became common practice for people living in malaria-infested areas along the Mississippi River to take quinine each day with breakfast. They found that by taking small daily doses they could avoid the chills, yet they were never cured, and they needed continuous treatment.

Dr. S.P.S. Edwards was a Seventh-day Adventist physician at the Tri-City Sanitarium in Moline, Illinois, from 1904 to 1909. Because of the writings of Ellen White, he refused to use quinine for malaria. Instead he used hydrotherapy. As more became known about malaria, several doctors began to use larger doses of quinine over a very short period of time and found that they could destroy the infective agent. Dr. Edwards tried coupling the larger short doses of quinine with hydrotherapy to overcome the side effects of the drug. His regimen was effective, saving the lives of many people. When Ellen White heard of the method that he was using successfully, she told him that what he was doing was different from what she referred to in her testimonies. She noted that, like using ether or chloroform for surgery, Edwards employed one or two doses to kill the cause, and did not continue to dose the patient day after day, as was done in so many places. Repeated drugging was what she had condemned, she said.[10]

A similar example was her acceptance of vaccinations for smallpox. While her hydropathic contemporaries were condemning vaccination, she herself was vaccinated and urged her domestic staff to do the same (see *Selected Messages,* book 2, p. 305). Ellen White was a progressive health reformer who praised God for scientific advances.

She even used a primitive form of radiation therapy for a skin lesion on her face. Perhaps she thought it was cancerous. In a letter to her son Edson in 1911 she states, "For several weeks I took treatment with the X-ray for the black spot that was on my forehead. In all I took twenty-three treatments, and these succeeded in entirely removing the mark. For this I am very grateful" (*Selected Messages,* book 2, p. 303). Apparently she did not consider using radiation therapy for a suspected cancer as inconsistent with her call for the use of simple remedies.

Ellen White never lost sight of the primary core of the message God gave her. It was and always will be the reformed style of living. Yes, modern advances would help with the treatment of disease, but preservation of health would still be through the natural remedies of exercise, fresh air, sunlight, a nutritious diet, and an abiding confidence in God. The Seventh-day Adventist reform movement survived and outlived all the other medical sects of the nineteenth century: the homeopath, the allopath, the phrenologist, the herbalist, and the like. It remained a movement that could encompass and incorporate scientific advances in the understanding of God's intricate creation.

New approaches to health. Ellen White counseled the church to develop a full program of medical education that would make it possible for practitioners to become licensed physicians and nurses. The new health reformers, they were to educate the church members, and together they were to be medical missionaries. "The light given me is, We must provide that which is essential to qualify our youth who desire to be physicians, so that they may intelligently fit themselves to be able to stand the examinations required to prove their efficiency as physicians. They should be taught to treat understandingly the cases of those who are diseased, so that the door will be closed for any sensible physician to imagine that we are not giving in our school the instruction necessary for properly qualifying young men and young women to do the work of a physician" (*Medical Ministry,* p. 57).

CONCLUSIONS

1. Natural remedies are first and foremost a lifestyle. They form

the centerpiece of the Seventh-day Adventist health-reform message.

2. Self-doctoring, or personal self-care, is still necessary. Health care will become more and more scarce as economics limit services to those individuals with the most acute and severe diseases. One way to deal with the shortage is to teach home remedies for the simple diseases. Sprains, bruises, bites, headaches, and flu can be cared for at home if the church has trained its members and their neighbors.

3. The wise use of pharmacological preparations is still important. However, many people use these preparations to excess. Whether Tylenol or goldenseal, both may be unnecessary if we still taught more simple therapies such as water cures.

4. Education in physiology is the greatest protection we can give against health fraud and quackery. It will also form a bulwark against spiritualistic healing methods.

5. Spiritual healing is the primary focus of all medical health work. We must give it the broad exposure and the emphasis that is essential for it.

6. There does not need to be a gulf between the use of the most advanced medical methods and the promotion of the simple self-care practices. Ellen White did not have a conflict between recommending that nurses learn to use herbs and at the same time urging a medical educational institution that had the highest reputation within the emerging American Medical Association. She could recommend to the church's leading physician the use of charcoal poultices for abdominal pain and receive the most advanced radiation therapy at the time for her skin lesion. The separation of preventive medicine, acute-care medicine, and self-care into often antagonistic, elitist camps is wrong, wasteful, and confusing.

---

[1] Sylvester Graham, *Lectures on the Science of Human Life* (New York: Fowler and Wells, 1851), p. 3.

[2] E. A. Sutherland, *Studies in Christian Education* (Leominster, Mass.: Eusey Press), p. 31.

[3] In a letter to Dr. J. H. Kellogg about the merits of charcoal, she wrote, "I expect you will laugh at this; but if I could give this remedy some outlandish name that no one knew but myself, it would have greater influence" (*Selected Messages,* book 2, p. 294).

[4] Dr. Merritt Kellogg sought the aid of Ellen White. He said, "Have you any light for me on this case? If relief cannot be given our sister, she can live but a few hours" (*ibid.,* p. 295).

[5] S. M. Pond, K. R. Olson, et al., "Randomized Study of the Treatment of

"I THINK I'LL DOCTOR MYSELF"

Phenobarbital Overdose With Repeated Doses of Activated Charcoal," *Journal of the American Medical Association* 251 (1982): 3104-3108; R. J. Hillman, "Treatment of Solicylate Poisoning With Repeated Oral Charcoal," *British Medical Journal* 291 (1985): 1472.

[6] P. Kuusisto, et al., in *Lancet* 1986; ii: 366.

[7] Varro E. Tyler, "False Tenets of Paraherbalism," *Nutrition Forum* 6 (1989): 41.

[8] Harry B. Weiss and Howard R. Kemble, *The Great American Water Cure Craze: A History of Hydropathy in the United States* (Trenton, N.J.: Past Times Press, 1967), p. 17.

[9] Francis Graetor, ed. and trans., *Hydriatics: Or Manual of the Water Cure, Especially as Practiced by Vincent Priessnitz at Gräefenberg, Silesia, Austria* (London: James Madden, 1942), p. 70.

[10] S.P.S. Edwards to F. D. Nichol, 1957.

Warren Peters is director of the Center for Health Promotion, Loma Linda University, Loma Linda, California.

Chapter 9

WHY A MINISTRY
OF HEALING?

Gary D. Strunk

Why should the Seventh-day Adventist Church, which God commissioned to preach the gospel of the judgment, promote a health and healing ministry? A healing ministry provides justification to expect miraculous healings, to labor continually to relieve human suffering, and especially to teach people the laws of life so as to prevent disease and allow nature's processes to overcome diseases of body, mind, and soul. When we combine teaching and healing, we have true ministry.

HEALTH IS GOD'S WILL

A health ministry that includes healing, disease prevention, and health enhancement needs to be built on the belief that good health is God's will. Death, disease, and suffering are the natural-law consequences of humanity's God-given freedom to choose to transgress the laws of life. Sin and its consequences, however, are contrary to God's will for His creatures. As we seek to relieve suffering and put a halt to sin we cooperate with His efforts to restore the universe to harmonious compliance with His laws of life.

Ellen White writes: "Disease never comes without a cause. The way is first prepared, and disease invited by disregarding the laws of health. God does not take pleasure in the sufferings and death of little children. He commits them to parents, for them to educate physically, mentally and morally, and train them for usefulness here, and for Heaven at last" (*Selected Messages,* book 2, p. 469).

WHY A MINISTRY OF HEALING?

SCRIPTURE PRECEDENT

Through His continuously operating power by which He upholds the universe (Heb. 1:3), God is the one who heals our diseases (Ps. 103:3). But at times He involves His servants in that ministry of healing, as He did with Moses and the brass serpent or Elisha and his many acts of healing.

Moses also taught health. He established an enviable health education program guided by priest-physicians who read its laws to the congregation every seven years (Deut. 31:9-12).

Teaching, preaching, and tireless restoration of the sick and suffering characterized Jesus' ministry (Matt. 4:23-25; 8:1-3, 14-16; Acts 10:38). He charged the apostles: "Preach, saying, The kingdom of heaven is at hand. Heal the sick, cleanse the lepers" (Matt. 10:7, 8), linking healing and preaching together. His commission to the 70 was: "Heal the sick . . . and say unto them, The kingdom of God is come nigh unto you" (Luke 10:9). Believers, He said, "shall lay hands on the sick, and they shall recover" (Mark 16:18). So by Jesus' example and His commission to preach, to teach, and to seek healing (verse 15; Matt. 28:20; see also James 5:14, 15), the church has received authorization to do all in its power to relieve pain and suffering and to help prevent illness and accident.

Ellen White supports this health emphasis. "Read the Scriptures carefully, and you will find that Christ spent the largest part of His ministry in restoring the suffering and afflicted to health. . . . We shall have success if we work on practical lines. Ministers, do not confine your work to giving Bible instruction. Do practical work. Seek to restore the sick to health. This is true ministry. Remember that the restoration of the body prepares the way for the restoration of the soul" (*Medical Ministry,* p. 240).

"Christ, the Great Medical Missionary, is our example. Of Him it is written that He 'went about all Galilee, teaching in their synagogues, and preaching the gospel of the kingdom, and healing all manner of sickness and all manner of disease among the people.' Matt. 4:23. He healed the sick and preached the gospel. In His service, healing and teaching were linked closely together. Today they are not to be separated" (*Counsels on Health,* pp. 395, 396).

"A gospel minister will be twice as successful in his work if he understands how to treat disease" *(Medical Ministry,* p. 245).

"Those who go forth to engage in work of the ministry must be intelligent upon the subject of health reform. Those men who after many years' experience have yet no appreciation of the medical missionary work, should not be appointed to preside over our churches" *(ibid.,* p. 238).

"There is a great work to be done. How shall we reveal Christ? I know of no better way . . . than to take hold of the medical missionary work in connection with the ministry. Wherever you go, there begin to work. Take an interest in those around you who need help and light. You may stand and preach to those here who know the truth; you may preach sermon after sermon to them, but they do not appreciate it. Why? Because they are inactive. Every one who is able to go out and work should bring to the foundation stone, not hay, wood, or stubble, but gold, silver, and precious stones" *(ibid.,* p. 319).

"The life of Christ and His ministry to the afflicted are inseparably connected. From the light that has been given me, I know that an intimate relationship should ever exist between the medical missionary work and the gospel ministry. They are bound together in sacred union as one work, and are never to be divorced. The principles of heaven are to be adopted and practiced by those who claim to walk in the Saviour's footsteps. By His example He has shown us that medical missionary work is not to take the place of the preaching of the gospel, but is to be bound up with it. Christ gave a perfect representation of true godliness by combining the work of a physician and a minister, ministering to the needs of both body and soul, healing physical disease, and then speaking words that brought peace to the troubled heart" *(Counsels on Health,* p. 528).

Love Responds to Human Need

Jesus said, "Love thy neighbor as thyself" (Matt. 19:19). Love alone is sufficient reason to help others overcome and avoid sickness and improve their health in every way possible.

Jesus responded to the cry of human need: " 'If you are willing, you can make me clean.' Filled with compassion, Jesus reached out his hand and touched the man. 'I am willing,' he said. 'Be clean!'" (Mark 1:40, 41, NIV). His response to the man exemplified His response to thousands and models what should be our response and responsibility to humanity's cry in both the developed and developing worlds.

In developing countries the need is obvious for more and better food, hygiene, and healthful conditions. Better health is a plaintive cry in America as well. Several years ago the University of Chicago, the YMCA schools, and the Adult Education Society conducted a large-scale survey over a period of two years, asking adults, should they have opportunity to go back to school, what topics they would most want to study. The number one response was health: "Teach us how to be healthy."

What about today? What is the answer for need number one? Better health. Health food stores have sprung up in every city and village. University newsletters, health magazines, health articles in every kind of magazine, and TV programs devoted to health demonstrate widespread interest in the subject. America's national health reform needs Adventist health reform.

In 1985 *Success* magazine surveyed its readers to learn what they felt were the symbols of success (October 1985, p. 46). Readers chose three out of 12 listed items. The highest-rated symbol of success was having good health.

Symbols of Success

Good health	58%
Enjoyable job	49%
Happy family	45%
Peace of mind	34%
Good friends	25%
Intelligence	15%
Unlimited money	11%
Talent	7%
Luck	6%
Luxury car	2%
Expensive home	1%

THE MASTER'S HEALING TOUCH

In 1984 Canada's *McLean* magazine asked its readers to choose a New Year's wish. Which would you rather have, better health, better love life, or more income? Forty-four percent said better health, 42 percent said better income, and 10 percent said better love life.

The Adventist Research Task Force (HART) in southern California in 1988 asked Mark Baldassare, associate professor of social ecology, University of California at Irvine, a noted and often-quoted survey research scientist, to conduct a study in Fullerton, California, to learn what a secular community would desire from the ideal church. The study determined that the ideal church in a secular community would conduct stress-control and health programs.

People are interested in health, and we are in position to reveal the love of God through it. The cry of human need is a Macedonian mandate to the Seventh-day Adventist Church. "I saw that it is the duty of those who have received the light from heaven and have realized the benefit of walking in it, to manifest a greater interest for those who are still suffering for want of knowledge. Sabbathkeepers who are looking for the soon appearing of their Saviour should be the last to manifest a lack of interest in this great work of reform. Men and women must be instructed, and ministers and people should feel that the burden of the work rests upon them to agitate the subject and urge it home upon others" *(Testimonies for the Church,* vol. 1, p. 489).

"THIS [HEALTH] IS YOUR WISDOM"

When God placed Israel at the crossroads of the nations, He said to them: "Behold, I have taught you statutes and judgments, even as the Lord my God commanded me, that ye should do so in the land whither ye go to possess it. Keep therefore and do them; for this is your wisdom and your understanding in the sight of the nations, which shall hear all these statutes, and say, Surely this great nation is a wise and understanding people. For what nation is there so great, who hath God so nigh unto them, as the Lord our God is in all things that we call upon him for? And what nation is there so great, that hath statutes and judgments so righteous as all this law, which I set before you this day?" (Deut. 4:5-8).

Through their good health, God has placed Seventh-day Adventists in the crossroads of interest of many nations. With the advent of statistics we can now document scientifically that Seventh-day Adventists are healthier and live longer than the average population in every country in which they have been studied. Consequently, we can show with scientific language the health advantage of following the Bible. Such scientific evidence provides to the world tangible, measurable, hard evidence that following the Bible is beneficial. It speaks loudly in a language that people of this generation understand. Adventists have received more press in scientific journals and in popular magazines and newspapers for their health than for any other thing they have done in the past 100 years. They are known for their health. Our health becomes our wisdom in the sight of the nations.

"If we backslide on this point [health reform], we lose much influence with the outside world" *(Counsels to Writers and Editors,* p. 126).

"The Lord desires through His people to answer Satan's charges by showing the result of obedience to right principles. . . . Seventh-day Adventists are to be represented to the world by the advance principles of health reform which God has given us" *(Medical Ministry,* p. 187).

"Seventh-day Adventists are handling momentous truths. . . . It is our duty to understand and respect the principles of health reform. On the subject of temperance we should be in advance of all other people" *(Testimonies for the Church,* vol. 9, p. 158).

LAST-DAY MINISTRY

A Ministry of Spiritual Gifts. The gifts of the Spirit are to be active in the church until the mission of the church is complete (Eph. 4:13). One of those gifts is healing (1 Cor. 12:9), and another is teaching (Eph. 4:11). Each gift is to contribute to building up the church both in quantity and quality, and it is reasonable that healing should be an active ministry of the church. Working on the assumption that healing should not happen without corollary instruction in the causes of illness and how to prevent further illness, it is logical that health education should be a vital ministry of the church as well.

COUNSEL FROM THE SPIRIT OF PROPHECY

We can derive our theology of health and healing entirely from the Bible, but we also have the advantage of the writings of Ellen White. Her messages forcefully direct our attention to the role, the importance, and the methods of achieving health. "I wish to tell you that soon there will be no work done in ministerial lines but medical missionary work" *(Counsels on Health,* p. 533).

A Ministry of Teaching. Because of the many healing miracles in the ministry of Jesus and the early church, one could well ask, "Why should not the Seventh-day Adventist Church seek to perform miracles rather than establish hospitals and do health education?"

First, the circumstances and beliefs of Jesus' day were different from ours today. People commonly believed that those who had serious diseases and infirmities had fallen under the curse of God and could not be saved. Therefore, Jesus healed prodigiously both Jew and Gentile to counter the prevailing belief. By healing them He removed the "curse" and conveyed the truth that God could forgive and save the sick.

Second, we can expect some miracles, but prophecies such as Revelation 13 tell us that deceptive miracles will help erect an image to the beast. The miracles that characterize the work of the beast include ones of healing that appear to ratify its doctrines as authentic. In contrast, Scripture depicts the followers of God as those who keep the commandments of God and have the testimony of Jesus (Rev. 14:12). To avoid the possibility of appearing like those who follow the beast, we would do well to stress the greater miracle of a regenerate heart that restores believers to harmony with the laws of God (Rom. 8:1-4), including His laws of nature, so that health and healing follow naturally.

Third, in the organization and education of Israel, God set forth a comprehensive proclamation of the laws of life (Rom. 7:10; Lev. 18:5) and promised freedom from disease on condition of obedience (Deut. 7:11-15; Ex. 15:26). It was and is God's preferred method of restoring people to health—through the natural results of intelligent obedience to the laws of life. Although a measure of divine interposition is still needed to enable people to obey and to protect them from illness, if people obeyed faithfully, miraculous healings would seldom be required.

Fourth, a health ministry implicitly conveys certain vital truths of the gospel better than miracles do. For example, it is only as people obey the laws of healthful living, not just know them, that they can expect to reap the benefits.

Fifth, a great part of the work of the gospel is to empower people to develop the fruit of the Spirit, which includes self-control (Gal. 5:23; 1 Tim. 3:2; 2 Peter 1:6), giving them direction over their lives and restoring them to obedience to the commandments of God and the laws of life. A teaching ministry does this more effectively than miracles do.

Last, Jesus was a health educator. He taught the law, and He taught a relationship between sin and disease (John 5:14). Also He gave instruction on how their needs were to be met (Matt. 6:33), which helps greatly to prevent physical, emotional, and spiritual sickness.

"To make natural law plain, and to urge obedience to it, is a work that accompanies the third angel's message. Ignorance is no excuse now for the transgression of law. The light shines clearly, and none need be ignorant; for the great God Himself is man's instructor. All are bound by the most sacred obligations to heed the sound philosophy and genuine experience which God is now giving them in reference to health reform. He designs that the subject shall be agitated and the public mind deeply stirred to investigate it; for it is impossible for men and women, while under the power of sinful, health-destroying, brain-enervating habits, to appreciate sacred truth" *(Counsels on Health,* p. 21).

"Jesus Christ is the Great Healer, but He desires that by living in conformity with His laws we may cooperate with Him in the recovery and the maintenance of health. Combined with the work of healing there must be an imparting of knowledge of how to resist temptations. Those who come to our sanitariums should be aroused to a sense of their own responsibility to work in harmony with the God of truth.

"We cannot heal. We cannot change the diseased conditions of the body. But it is our part, as medical missionaries, as workers together with God, to use the means that He has provided. Then we should pray that God will bless these agencies. We do believe in a God; we believe in a God who hears and answers prayer. He has said, 'Ask, and ye shall receive; seek, and ye shall find; knock, and it shall be opened unto you'" (*Medical Ministry*, p. 13).

WHOLE-BIBLE CHRISTIANS

So what should the church teach? Nearly all the laws of the Pentateuch affect the health of body, mind, and soul. We find there principles of personal hygiene, public sanitation, diet, work and rest regulations, quarantine, and other measures of disease control. Also we encounter rules of life-governing emotional health, social relations, and spiritual life. Although Scripture does not mention health in direct connection with any one of these laws, nevertheless, God promises freedom from disease along with productivity and prosperity (both by natural effect and miraculous intervention) if we will obey these laws, commandments, and statutes (Deut. 7:11-15).

Jesus endorsed those laws when He said, "Think not that I am come to destroy the law, or the prophets: I am not come to destroy, but to fulfil" (Matt. 5:17). Although certain rituals and regulations lost their relevancy at the cross and the dispersion of the Jewish nation, Christ never lifted the ban on fat, blood, or unclean meats, for neither human physiology nor the habits of pigs and other scavengers changed when Jesus died on the cross.

Christ did not give His laws in the Old Testament and then replace them in the New Testament. The original ones are still effectual and should be included as the teachings of Christ to His followers.

"Christ had been the guide and teacher of ancient Israel, and He taught them that health is the reward of obedience to the laws of God. The great Physician who healed the sick in Palestine had spoken to His people from the pillar of cloud, telling them what they must do, and what God would do for them. 'If thou wilt diligently hearken to the voice of the Lord thy God,' He said, 'and wilt do that which is right in his sight, and wilt give ear to his commandments, and keep all his statutes, I will put none of these diseases upon thee, which I have brought upon the Egyptians; for I am the Lord that healeth thee.' Christ gave to Israel definite instruction in regard to their habits of life, and He assured them, 'The Lord will take away from thee all sickness.' When they fulfilled the conditions, the promise was verified to them. 'There was not one feeble person among their tribes'" *(Counsels on Diet and Foods,* p. 121).

LET YOUR LIGHT SHINE

Although Jesus genuinely ministered to people's physical needs, healing their infirmities and feeding the 5,000, His higher objective was to give them eternal life. Likewise, God's health ministry, if it is to fulfill its Heaven-ordained purpose, is to (1) genuinely benefit people, (2) be conducted by the church, a religious institution, and not separate from the church, and (3) point sin-sick souls to the Man of Calvary, who takes away the sin of the world.

"We should ever remember that the object of the medical missionary work is to point sin-sick men and women to the Man of Calvary, who taketh away the sin of the world" *(ibid.,* p. 458).

"We are to do all in our power for the healing of the body; but we are to make the healing of the soul of far greater importance" *(Testimonies for the Church,* vol. 7, p. 96).

"The sick need to have wise words spoken to them. Nurses should study the Bible daily, that they may be able to speak words that will enlighten and help the suffering. . . .

"They should uplift the standard of temperance from a Christian point of view, showing that the body is the temple of the Holy Spirit and bringing to the minds of the people the responsibility resting upon them as God's purchased possession to make mind and body a holy temple, fit for the indwelling of the Holy Spirit. When temperance is presented as a part of the gospel, many will see their need to reform. . . . As this instruction is given, the people will become interested in other lines of Bible study" *(ibid.,* p. 75).

SUMMARY

God is intensely interested in our total well-being. His detailed health instructions in the Bible, the healing ministry of the prophets and of Jesus, and His commissions to heal, teach, and preach, plus the love within our hearts for our neighbor and the plaintive cry of human need, provide powerful justification for the Seventh-day Adventist Church to be highly active in a health ministry. Jesus has personally blessed Seventh-day Adventists with messages from His own lips, enabling His remnant church to enjoy a measurable advantage in health and longevity, which sends a signal to the world in scientific language that they can understand that God's Word is relevant and beneficial in these last days. Seventh-day Adventists, taking the whole Bible as their guide, are to flow out in streams of living water to the world, healing, teaching, and preaching in the name of Jesus Christ. This is true ministry!

Gary Strunk is director of religious studies at the Pacific Health Education Center, Bakersfield, California.

Chapter 10

QUACKS AND OTHER CHARLATANS

William T. Jarvis, Ph.D.

He appeared out of nowhere at the school up in the highlands. "It took me three days in this country," he said to its faculty, "to find anything fit to eat according to Ellen White's health principles.

"I am here," he continued, "to teach the students the true principles of health. Not only that, but I can look into their eyes, diagnose illnesses, and pinpoint where the illness is hiding in the body.

"This," he said, "is true health reform, and the Lord has sent me here to teach it to your students."

The school officials were not too sure, however! They wondered if the so-called Ellen White-approved food he found after searching for three days was really that much different, or if hunger may have caused him to evaluate it on a different scale! Was this a healer himself in need of healing?

What is a "quack"? It is "anyone who promotes medical schemes or remedies known to be false or unproven."[1] The current interest among the general public in healthful living has produced an increasing number of questionable alternative healing practices and get-well-quick schemes, "spiritual" healing methods connected with the New Age movement, and an array of other options. What should be the Seventh-day Adventist response to all this? Does our health message naturally lead us toward these types of healing peculiarities, or should we be increasingly careful to make sure we don't follow healers in need of healing?

Ellen White was very critical of quackery. She directed statements against the patent medicine cure-alls of her day. Her condemnation of "drugs" largely focused on the narcotics and poison stimulants used to mask the symptoms of illnesses while having no beneficial effects on the diseases themselves. She also wrote in favor of licensure laws that protect the public from unqualified practitioners: "Wise laws have been framed in order to safeguard the people against the imposition of unqualified physicians. These laws we should respect, for we are ourselves by them protected from presumptuous pretenders" *(Medical Ministry,* p. 84). A substantial amount of modern-day quackery has its roots in pantheistic belief systems, and its apparent success is due to the same psychological principles that make occult practices appear to work.

OCCULT PRACTICES

Occult practices refer to "matters regarded as involving the action or influence of supernatural agencies or some secret knowledge of them"[2] and to the things done by shamans, pagan priests, mediums, mystics, stargazers, sorcerers, seers, soothsayers, oracles, and the like, to validate themselves and their methods. Occult practices are increasingly popular, especially horoscopes and psychics who advertise on TV and almost all communication media.

Much of what such practitioners do is clever and represents psychological trickery. Occult practitioners almost always leave themselves an out for explaining away apparent failures. Astrologers are fond of saying that the "stars portend but they don't compel." When horoscopes fail, they can always fall back on this ancient escape clause.

THE NEED FOR SKEPTICISM

The word "skeptic" derives from the Greek word *skeptomai,* which meant to "look at something carefully" and "examine" and "consider" it.[3] Christians generally hesitate to label themselves as "skeptics," fearing that skepticism shows a lack of faith. This need not be. Traditionally Adventism has demanded that faith be soundly based upon evidence from Scripture and the natural world, believing that God is rational, orderly, and reasonable.

QUACKS AND OTHER CHARLATANS

Adventists reject religious systems that emphasize subjective personal experience as the most important guide in one's life as irrational and unrepresentative of a God of reason.

THE ART OF DECEPTION AND THE OCCULT

Ancient occult practitioners were masters of the art of deception. Keen observers, stargazers kept records and eventually realized that heavenly movements followed regular patterns. The priests were able to predict eclipses of the sun and moon. This special knowledge enabled them to claim to cause the eclipses and then to save the heavenly bodies from danger. Thus the alleged mystic took credit for a natural phenomenon and attained great stature in the eyes of the uninformed.

Ancient medicine also used occult practices. Greek priest-physicians at the temples of Asclepius doped the ill with opium. The opium stupor relieved suffering and led patients to misperceive what they saw. Harmless serpents slithered around the patients. Patients believed that the serpents would lick their ailing bodies as they wagged their forked tongues. This no doubt had a dramatic psychological effect. Patients also passed through dark tunnels in which hidden practitioners whispered words of encouragement. The sick concluded that they were hearing the voices of the gods and that they would be healed.

Today we recognize that magical beliefs and practices are part of psychosomatic medicine (medicine that uses the mind to help heal the body). The ancients sincerely believed in their magic and assumed that they were rendering a higher level of treatment than anything done to the physical body. They were treating the ethereal "soul" ("spirit," "psyche," "mind"). Such a view has revived under the banner of New Age health care. Its followers use mystical interpretations that claim the existence of an immortal soul alleged to be a manifestation of a universal life force. Some extol mind-altering drugs as a means of getting in touch with the "spiritual dimension." Today science knows that altered mind states that believers assume are out-of-body experiences (e.g., astral projection, near-death mind/body separations) actually result from diminished oxygen levels in the brain and can be duplicated experimentally.

THE MASTER'S HEALING TOUCH

SELF-DECEPTION

Studying the confessions of con artists leads to the conclusion that much deception includes a degree of self-deception. Many who start out intentionally to deceive eventually come to believe that what they do is socially justifiable or even more honest than the hypocrisy they see within society.

A young woman who had come to believe in iridology had demonstrated her practice on several graduate nursing students. She explained that she had become convinced of the validity of iridology after examining a person in whom she detected an un-apparent problem with her left leg. Startled, the woman she had been examining said she had been afflicted with polio as a child. She explained that her left leg had been affected, but that she had rehabilitated it and the condition was no longer noticeable. A dramatic thing happened next. One of the nurses the practi-tioner had also just examined informed her that as a child she too had come down with polio and had once limped badly, but had rehabilitated her leg. However, the iridologist had *not* de-tected it during her iridology examination. The revelation left the iridologist speechless.

PROTECTION FROM DECEPTION

Unfortunately, some health-conscious Seventh-day Adventists do not discriminate between sound and fake health ideas. Instead of "testing all things," they seek "peculiarity" for its own sake. In my study of the psychology of deception, I have found one supreme rule that serves as a guide: "For the mystery of iniquity doth already work: only he who now letteth will let, until he be taken out of the way. And then shall that Wicked be revealed, whom the Lord shall consume with the spirit of his mouth, and shall destroy with the brightness of his coming: even him, whose coming is after the working of Satan with all power and signs and lying wonders, and with all deceivableness of unrighteousness in them that perish; because they received not the love of the *truth*, that they might be saved. And for this cause God shall send them strong delusion, that they should believe a lie: that they might all be damned who believed not the truth" (2 Thess. 2:7-12).

QUACKS AND OTHER CHARLATANS

SOME TRICKS OF THE TRADE

Cold Reading. Cold reading practitioners read the patient's pulses in the same way tea leaves are read. They offer hope and encouragement by providing diagnoses and remedies. The practitioner asks a lot of questions without committing himself or herself until the patient responds.

Telling People What They Want to Hear. Many patients want to occupy the role of being physically ill. *Somatizers* are people with psychosocial (i.e., personality or behavioral) problems who refuse to accept a diagnosis. Somatization explains why many patients readily accept misdiagnoses by quack doctors. Society's tendency to view people with psychological problems as being inferior encourages the denial of psychiatric disorder. Stewart[4] found that about 60 percent of sufferers are amenable to treatment, but the others refuse to relinquish their diagnoses for self-serving reasons.

The P. T. Barnum Effect. P. T. Barnum was the founder of a world-famous circus. A circus sideshow fools people because they want to be fooled. For instance, an astrology book offers the following stock speech as a personality reading for college-aged clients: "Some of your aspirations tend to be pretty unrealistic. At times you are extroverted, affable, sociable, while at other times you are introverted, wary, and reserved. You have found it unwise to be too frank in revealing yourself to others. You pride yourself on being an independent thinker and do not accept others' opinions without satisfactory proof. You prefer a certain amount of change and variety, and become dissatisfied when hemmed in by restrictions and limitations. At times you have serious doubts as to whether you have made the right decision or done the right thing. Disciplined and controlled on the outside, you tend to be worrisome and insecure on the inside. Your sexual adjustment has presented some problems for you. While you have some personal weaknesses, you are generally able to compensate for them. You have a great deal of unused capacity which you have not turned to your advantage. You have a tendency to be critical of yourself. You have a strong need for other people to like you and for them to admire you."[5] While it fits just about any college-aged person, researchers found that people rated this description significantly higher if they believed it had been written for them personally.[6]

The One-sided Coin Toss (heads, I win; tails, you lose). The one-sided coin toss is a *no-fail* tactic in which the practitioner leads the patient to think a desirable outcome will result, but at the same time leaves room for an opposite interpretation. Since diseases, sometimes even serious ones such as cancer, are self-limiting, some individuals get well apart from anything medical practitioners do. If one notes only successes, a false illusion will make it appear that a certain healing system is effective when it really isn't. Those who spontaneously recover can present impressive testimonials that offer convincing evidence that the therapeutic system has value (the "it worked for me" scenario). However, such an approach never considers failures. As one "holistic" medical doctor explained to a colleague whose patient wasn't responding to her favorite therapy: "When the spirit gets ready to leave the body, there is little we can do!"

Dr. Feelgood. Health-conscious people generally reject drugs as incompatible with a healthy lifestyle, but seekers of superhealth are being fooled by herbal drug pushers. A study of health practices and beliefs[7] revealed that people do not differentiate between symptomatic relief and truly effective remedies. Subjectively feeling good is the gauge many use to evaluate whether a practice is good or bad. Large numbers of people mistakenly believe that it is possible to gain vigor and energy by simply improving one's diet or using special supplements instead of following a broad healthy lifestyle. They want shortcuts, and seek them in supplements or special herbal products. Many popular herbal products contain potent stimulant drugs that consumers fail to recognize because the products are sold as "foods," or because they have been called "herbs." Feel-good herbs include ginseng, broom, mate, lettuce opium, lobelia, valerian, and coffee enemas.

Personal Self-deception. Personal self-deception begins with a deluded self-concept. *To become, act as if!* To become a millionaire, "think, act, and feel like a millionaire!" "Sleep in the biggest bed imaginable." "Buy the biggest or best washcloth, towel, soap, razor, toothbrush, and/or shaving lotion available." "Spread dollars' worth of change in all the places you look daily. . . . Put a $100 bill in your billfold. . . . Let this system remind you everywhere you turn that you are becoming a millionaire."

PANTHEISM

Worshiping the creation rather than the Creator has characterized paganism since antiquity. Idolatry involved the worship of images made by human hand. Isaiah describes idolatry: "He burneth part thereof in the fire; with part thereof he eateth flesh; he roasteth roast, and is satisfied: yea, he warmeth himself, and saith, Aha, I am warm, I have seen the fire: and the residue thereof he maketh a god, even his graven image: he falleth down unto it, and worshippeth it, and prayeth unto it, and saith, Deliver me; for thou art my god" (Isa. 44:16, 17).

Monism. Monism holds that only one fundamental reality exists, that it is inseparable or indivisible, and essentially metaphysical and mystical. This belief that likeness possessed *essence* (i.e., life force) is the basis for the third commandment, which forbids not only the worship of these images but even their manufacture.

Pantheism and monism are harmonious worldviews. The basis of pantheism is the concept that God is a universal life force. It denies the personal nature of God with attributes of character such as righteousness, mercy, love, justice, and generosity, and is incompatible with the belief in Jesus Christ as God incarnate. Little wonder that Ellen White so strongly condemned pantheism: "[Pantheistic] theories, followed to their logical conclusion, sweep away the whole Christian economy" (*Testimonies for the Church,* vol. 8, p. 291); and "Not one thread of [it] is to be drawn into the web" (*Medical Ministry,* p. 98).

The public is so enamored with the word "natural" that it has become a marketing term that helps to sell everything from underwear to cigars. However, are "natural" things always superior to "human-made," "cultivated," or "civilized" things? Let nature grow your garden, and you will share it with weeds, insects, birds, and foraging animals, and you will starve.

THE MASTER'S HEALING TOUCH

HEALTH-RELATED MANIFESTATIONS OF MONISM

Monism, with its pantheistic overtones, is central to many ancient cosmologies, including practices related to health and disease.

Vitalism. The idea of a metaphysical life force is not limited to religious ideologies, but has been secularized in the form of *vitalism*. Vitalism is a doctrine that the functions of a living organism are a result of a vital principle distinct from physicochemical forces.[8] Such a doctrine opposes modern science's mechanistic approach to physiology and views life as primarily metaphysical and mystical. Even many atheistic scientists hold vitalistic worldviews, including a persistent interest in extrasensory perception (ESP). For example, many Russian scientists interested in ESP use the word "bioplasma" to describe the life force.

The chart below shows where some of these ideas come from:

TITLE	ORIGIN
prana	Hinduism (Ayurvedic medicine)
chi (Ki, Qi)	Taoism and Chinese medicine
mana	Polynesian
orenda	Native American (Indian)
animal magnetism	Franz Anton Mesmer
the innate	D. D. Palmer, founder of chiropractics
orgone energy	Wilhelm Reich
vital energy	Samuel Hahnemann, founder of homeopathy
odic force	Baron Karl von Reichenbach
vis medicatrix naturea	naturopathy
bioplasma	contemporary Russian para-psychologists

Folk Medicine. Folk medicine is the use of various remedies by "healers" who form part of the social structure of most societies. Much folk medicine finds its basis in monism. It uses specific parts of animals' bodies in the belief that there will be a transference of the likeness to the user. The heart of a tiger may be eaten in the hope of gaining courage, an umbilical cord ingested to aid in childbirth, or genitals to improve fertility. In fact, several animal species are on the endangered list because people poach them for their symbolic body parts.

A fundamental difference between Seventh-day Adventist philosophy and monism appears in the way Adventists view the use of mood-modifying drugs (excluding, of course, physician-prescribed-and-monitored antidepressants). From the Adventist viewpoint, mind-altering substances producing hallucination, trance, stupor, "high," or whatever affect the brain, thus distorting a person's view of reality, clouding the judgment, and diminishing an individual's ability to reason and act responsibly.

HEALTH-CARE PRACTICES FOUNDED UPON MONISM/VITALISM

Many common health-care practices operate on the principles of monism and vitalism, yet escape detection by the general public.

Acupuncture. Acupuncture's basis lies in ancient Chinese medicine that formed part of ancient Chinese religion or cosmology. This cosmology includes the concepts of yin and yang, two fundamental forces that generate all of the processes in the universe, and chi, the universal, invisible life energy said to flow through the body along 12 invisible channels or meridians, each associated with a particular organ. This theoretical basis of Chinese cosmology is scientifically groundless.

Animal Magnetism. Franz Anton Mesmer, an Austrian physician, conceived the concept of animal magnetism in the 1770s. In experimenting with the magnet, he got the idea that the human hand possessed a similar power.[9] The word "animal" derives from the Latin word *anima,* meaning "spirit" or "soul." Mesmer promoted the idea of a subtle, universal substance that gives things life and vitality. Sickness results from its loss or imbalance, and the strength of animal magnetism is to awaken latent powers that enable people to penetrate universal mysteries, to experience extrasensory perception and precognition, and to heal.[10] Ellen White clearly associated animal magnetism with evil *(Mind, Character, and Personality,* vol 1, p. 20).

Ayurvedic Medicine. Ayurveda means "knowledge of life" in Sanskrit. It is ancient Indian medicine now promoted by the Maharishi Ayurveda Corporation of America. They are the people who also advocate transcendental meditation (TM). Its primary methodology involves "pulse diagnosis." After taking a person's pulse, "doshas" are established. The theory is that there are three governing principles to every person called "vata," "kapha," and "pitta." Two of them dominate every individual. Vata relates to movement, circulation, nerve impulses, and respiration. Kapha has to do with solidarity, muscularity, and physical strengths, while pitta is associated with digestion and metabolism.

HOMEOPATHY

Homeopathy was the brainchild of Samuel Hahnemann in 1810. Dissatisfied with the "heroic medicine" of his time, in which physicians bled, purged, blistered, and puked their patients, Hahnemann searched for a new medical theory. Rediscovering the monistic concept of the ancients that "like cures like," he reasoned that medicinal agents could be matched with the illnesses they would benefit by giving drugs to healthy individuals and observing their symptoms. Quinine produced symptoms similar to malaria, which it was also known to alleviate. He also believed that the smaller the dose, the greater effect it would have upon sick people.

Hahnemann was also a pantheist. Modern homeopaths use his philosophical beliefs to justify their nonscientific practices: "Hahnemann . . . is . . . a child of the modern age of natural science, and adept in the chemistry of his day. . . . But he can still hold a conviction that an immaterial vital entity animates our organism until death when the purely chemical forces prevail and decompose it. . . . This vital entity which he characterizes as immaterial, spirit-like, and which maintains in health the harmonious wholeness of the organism, is in fact the wholeness of it."[11]

FOOT REFLEXOLOGY AND IRIDOLOGY

Foot reflexology, also called "zone therapy," alleges that reflex points to each of the body's organs have been superimposed on the human foot.

Iridology is a method that alleges to be able to diagnose diseases by examining the eye's iris. Proponents say that they can not only detect existing diseases but also find weaknesses in organ systems that can forecast disease well in advance of its clinical manifestations. We have no valid evidence that it works and some solid evidence that it doesn't.[12]

NATUROPATHY

Naturopathy doesn't have an identifiable founder. However, its roots are firmly set in monism with its pantheistic overtones. "Orthodox medicine assumes that the world is chaotic, mechanistic," writes a naturopathic physician. "We believe in the Vital Force which has inherent organization, is intelligent and intelligible. Our way is to research the mystery and beauty of the life force, in which we have faith. Our power and our responsibility is to bring the life force into the light."[13]

"HEALTH FOODS"

A great deal of philosophical ideology lurks in the health food movement. The strong commitment to items such as fertile eggs, raw milk, unprocessed foods, "organically grown" foods, "natural" vitamins, and so forth indicates a metaphysical approach to nutrition. Health food promoters refer to "Life Force" in their advertising more and more. Some health food stores stock books and magazines that promote mystical philosophies of health and various forms of quackery.

IMPLICATIONS FOR THE CHURCH

Not all Adventists agree regarding the kind of health care Adventist institutions should practice. A number are highly critical of the strong scientific orientation of the regular Adventist health-care system and seek to displace it with other approaches. Some of these involve the hydropathic (water cure) methods formerly employed at Battle Creek Sanitarium or emphasize prevention through rather extreme lifestyle changes. Sadly, still others indiscriminately employ nonscientific practices with many of the abuses we have described.

Dedicated Adventist researchers, physicians, dentists, public health specialists, and others continue the sound, scientifically based health-care system begun by our predecessors. Methods change because we progress with new insights into health care. Adventist health care grows because it is compatible with a scientific worldview. Both science and Adventism believe in a material reality and reject an ethereal reality as occult and mystical. And both science and Adventism see truth as progressive and place a higher priority on the commitment to truth and the process of discovering what is true than any past dogma that sought to define truth.

Science, however, is not religion. Here Adventists go beyond science to a belief in God. Not a "life force," but a personal God with attributes of character such as love, mercy, justice, generosity, and righteousness (integrity) that His followers seek to emulate.

[1] C. Pepper, *Quackery: A $10 Billion Scandal* (Subcommittee on Health and Long-term Care of the Select Committee on Aging, United States House of Representatives, No. 98-435, 1984).

[2] *Webster's New Collegiate Dictionary.*

[3] W. Funk, *Word Origins* (New York: Bell Publishing Co., 1978).

[4] D. E. Stewart, "Psychiatric Assessment of Patients With '20th-Century Disease' (Total Allergy Syndrome)," *Canadian Medical Association Journal* 133 (1985): 1,000-1,006; "Environmental Hypersensitivity Disorder, Total Allergy and 20th-Century Disease: A Critical Review," *Canadian Family Physician* 33 (1987): 405-410; "The Changing Faces of Somatization," *Psychosomatics* 31 (1990): 153-158; "Emotional Disorders Misdiagnosed as Physical Illness: Environmental Hypersensitivity, Candidiasis Hypersensitivity, and Chronic Fatigue Syndrome," *International Journal of Mental Health* 19 (1990): 56-68.

[5] R. Hyman, "The Cold Reading: How to Convince Strangers That You Know All About Them," *The Zetetic* 1 (1977): 18-37.

[6] C. R. Snyder and R. J. Shenkel, "The P. T. Barnum Effect," *Psychology Today,* March 1975.

[7] National Analysts, Inc., *A Study of Health Practices and Opinions* (Springfield, Va.: National Technical Information Service, 1972).

[8] *Webster's New Collegiate Dictionary.*

[9] F. H. Garrison, *History of Medicine* (Philadelphia: W. B. Saunders Co., 1929), p. 368.

[10] R. S. Ellwood, *Alternative Altars: Unconventional and Eastern Spirituality in America* (University of Chicago, 1979), pp. 91, 92.

[11] L. R. Twentyman, "The Nature of Homeopathy," *Royal Society of Health Journal* 102 (1982): 221-225.

QUACKS AND OTHER CHARLATANS

[12] A. Simon, D. M. Worthen, and J. A. Mitas, "An Evaluation of Iridology" *Journal of the American Medical Association* 242 (1979): 1385-1389.

[13] Pam Snider, *Into the Light*. In *Townsend Letter for Doctors* (1991 American Association of Naturopathic Physicians Convention, April 1992), p. 261.

William T. Jarvis, Ph.D, is professor of health promotion and education at Loma Linda University School of Public Health, Loma Linda, California, and president of the National Council Against Health Fraud, Inc.

Chapter 11

HEALTH AND SALVATION
—NO CONFLICT

Dalton D. Baldwin, Ph.D.

You believe in righteousness by glutenburger," charged a colleague. The circle of ministers laughed. The comic contrast between faith and glutenburger set them off. Some of them laughed in approval of the ironic suggestion that health has nothing to do with salvation.

What is the relation of the scientific pursuit of health to salvation by grace through faith? The subject is important for two reasons. First, pursuing health all too often becomes legalistic. Second, a faulty understanding of the nature of faith sometimes leads to the conclusion that health has nothing to do with salvation. We need a concept of faith that will guard against legalism and at the same time promote health.

Salvation by Faith Without Works

Paul's teaching that we are saved by faith alone without works of law applies also to health laws. Those who try to earn salvation by works of health law are legalistic and doomed to failure (Rom. 3:28; Gal. 2:16).

The apostle explained that those who tried to be righteous by keeping the law "did not succeed in fulfilling that law. Why not? Because they did not strive for [righteousness] on the basis of faith, but as if it were based on works" (Rom. 9:31, 32).*

God saves us by faith through the atonement of Christ without works of health law or any other law.

HEALTH AND SALVATION—NO CONFLICT

FAITH PRECEDES WORKS

One of the reasons we are saved by faith without works of law is that saving faith must precede deeds to make them possible. Paul found righteousness by faith taught in the Old Testament. His primary texts were the experiences of Abraham receiving the covenant and Habakkuk receiving the revelation that the righteous live by faith (Gen. 15; 17; Hab. 2:4).

When Paul pointed out that Abraham was righteous through faith commitment before the performance of circumcision, he stressed the fact that salvation precedes works (Rom. 4:9-11).

Paul discussed the sequence of learning and responding to truth in another passage in Romans. It has implications for a scientific approach to truth.

Everyone who calls on the name of the Lord shall be saved, he reminds us. But how are they to *call* on one in whom they have not believed? How are they to *believe* in one about whom they have never heard? How are they to *hear* without someone to proclaim Him? And how are they to *proclaim* Him unless God sends them? (Rom. 10:13-15).

We then have the following sequence:

- Someone **proclaims** a message.
- We **hear** the message.
- We **believe** the message.
- We **make a commitment** that acts on the message.

From this sequence in Romans we may generalize four steps in a method for evaluating and responding to truth.

Define the problem. The Bible warns that we should not believe everyone who proclaims something. When Paul came to Berea and claimed that God had sent him to preach that Jesus was the Christ, the listeners realized that they had a problem. Was Paul's message true? Had he been sent by God? A clear understanding of the nature of the problem is a step toward its solution. In step one we clearly state the problem.

Propose possible solutions. The next step in the Romans sequence involves *hearing*. It is necessary to understand the message in order to make a judgment about whether it has come from

God or not. Understanding the message gets the alternatives clearly in mind. Possible solutions to the Berean problem could have been: Paul's message was truth from God, it was not true, or it was partly true. In the second step we propose possible solutions to the problem.

Select the best solution. *Believing* is the next step in the Romans sequence. Since we should "not believe every Spirit" (1 John 4:1), we should "test everything" (1 Thess. 5:21). The noble Bereans tested Paul's claims and "examined the scriptures every day to see whether these things were so" (Acts 17:11). A basic test of truth claims is consistency with prior revelation (Isa. 8:19, 20; 1 Cor. 14:37, 38). We should select for adoption the solution most consistent with prior revelation.

However, *believing* is used in two different ways. Sometimes believing expresses mere mental assent without any commitment. For example, certain Jerusalem authorities "believed" in Jesus, but for fear of being put out of the synagogue they did not confess, or acknowledge, it (John 12:42). They merely arrived at a correct conclusion about Jesus without commitment. Belief as mere mental assent is the "dead" faith that James says even demons possess (James 2:17-19).

At other times "believing" in the Bible goes beyond mere mental assent to commitment in action. Here we appropriate a right conclusion as a principle of action. For example, Jesus promised that everyone who believes in the only Son will have eternal life (John 3:16).

In step three we believe only in the sense of arriving at a sound conclusion. We select the best solution.

Commitment in action. In Paul's sequence in Romans, calling follows belief. "Everyone who calls on the name of the Lord shall be saved" (Rom. 10:13).

I have vivid memories of an experience that illustrates the difference between mental assent and commitment in action. Bob threw my precious teddy bear up on the roof. I felt so sorry for my teddy up in that scary place. Dad lifted me as high as he could, and I managed to squirm up onto the roof. After hugging my teddy, I then crept back to the edge of the roof. It was such a long way down to the ground! Dad told me to jump, and he would catch me. I drew back.

"Do you believe I will catch you?" he asked.

"Yes," I whimpered.

"Then jump," he reassured me. Finally I made the commitment and jumped.

Dead faith merely assents in mind. Saving faith appropriates the gospel truth so that it becomes a principle of action.

Apparently Paul's enemies claimed that his doctrine of righteousness by faith encouraged people to sin, since they were not under law but under grace. Horrified, he explained: "Do you not know that if you present yourselves to anyone as obedient slaves, you are slaves of the one whom you obey, either of sin, which leads to death, or of obedience, which leads to righteousness? But thanks be to God that you, having once been slaves of sin, have become obedient from the heart to the form of teaching to which you were entrusted" (Rom. 6:16, 17).

The commitment to obey from the heart received the gift of saving faith. Reversing that commitment by deciding to sin broke the faith relationship and led to death. In the fourth step we respond to gospel truth by making a commitment that leads to action.

Evaluation of consequences. From the teaching of Jesus, we may add a fifth step to the sequence for evaluating and responding to truth. He taught that we could distinguish true prophets from false ones by evaluating the consequences of acting on their messages. "You will know them by their fruits" (Matt. 7:16).

I present the five steps derived from Romans and the teachings of Jesus in the middle column of the following table. They are strikingly similar to the description of a scientific method in the third column.

Sequence in Romans	A Biblical Method	A Scientific Method
Someone proclaims a message	1. Define the problem	1. Define the problem
We hear the message	2. Propose possible solutions	2. Propose possible solutions
We believe the message	3. Select the best solution	3. Select the best solution
We make a commitment that acts on the message	4. Commitment in solution	4. Try out the best solution
	5. Evaluate consequences	5. Evaluation

It should not surprise us that a biblical method of identifying and responding to truth is essentially a scientific method, since science developed out of the Judeo-Christian tradition. The crucial difference between the two lists occurs at step four. Faith in Paul's message to the Bereans required total commitment from the center of the being as a matter of eternal life or death. The scientist often tries out alternative solutions without any real personal commitment. However, the scientist who makes a commitment in action on all known truth will live longer and think and act more efficiently. At the same time the quality of the concepts of truth in faith decisions will improve if we guide them by disciplined science. Scientists should be persons of faith, and pilgrims of faith should be scientific.

The Bible teaches that understanding precedes faith commitment. This understanding includes careful—even scientific—testing. It also teaches that saving faith precedes the performance of works, or deeds.

Through the influence of predestinarian theologians such as Augustine, Luther, and Calvin, many Christians hold that faith precedes understanding. If we make the commitment of faith prior to testing, we open ourselves to delusions such as those of Jim Jones's People's Temple and the Branch Davidians.

HEALTH AND SALVATION—NO CONFLICT

FAITH COMMITMENT RECEIVES NEW CREATION

One of the reasons saving faith must precede deeds is that true obedience is possible only through the new creation received in faith. Jesus told Nicodemus that "no one can see the kingdom of God without being born from above" (John 3:3).

The new creation is so radical that Scripture describes it with the metaphor of new birth. Paul says that those who are saved are "in Christ" (Rom. 8:1), and "if anyone is in Christ, there is a new creation" (2 Cor. 5:17).

God gives the capacity to use free will to make faith decisions to every human being, no matter how sinful. If we use free will to choose faith, God grants us the gift of God's righteousness (Rom. 10:3).

He creates new structures in the nervous system that renew the mind (Rom. 12:2) and produce new feelings and behaviors. God's righteousness empowers the obedience of faith. Paul introduced and concluded his letter to the Romans by saying that God had called him to "bring about the obedience of faith" among the Gentiles (Rom. 1:5; 16:26).

THE SUBJECT MATTER OF FAITH

We can learn about the subject matter of faith decisions by analyzing biblical examples. The best-known and best-loved text in the Bible says, "For God so loved the world that he gave his only Son, so that everyone who believes in him may not perish but may have eternal life" (John 3:16).

Though the most frequently mentioned subject of faith decisions in the New Testament is Jesus Christ, a number of accounts of faith include no explicit reference to Him. When God offered Abraham a covenant, the account says, "And he believed the Lord; and the Lord reckoned it to him as righteousness" (Gen. 15:6). His faith commitment involved deciding whether or not to keep the covenant. We find no reference to the Messiah in the account.

At Kadesh Barnea God invited the children of Israel to possess the Promised Land. The account says, "You rebelled against the commandment of the Lord your God, and did not believe him nor obey his voice" (Deut. 9:23, NKJV). The letter to the

Hebrews explained that they did not enter the Promised Land because they rejected faith (Heb. 4:2). Their faith decision chose whether or not to enter the Promised Land.

When the Moabites and the Ammonites threatened to destroy Judah, God sent the prophet Jehaziel with a message of deliverance. Jehoshaphat celebrated by proclaiming, "Believe in the Lord your God, and you will be established; believe his prophets, and you will succeed" (2 Chron. 20:20, RSV). Prophetic instruction is another subject matter for faith decisions.

The lame man at the pool received healing by faith when he responded to the instruction of Jesus: "Stand up, take your mat and walk" (John 5:8). When the rulers asked who healed him, he "did not know who it was" (verse 13). We know, therefore, that he had no consciousness of the life, death, and resurrection of Jesus in his faith decision. His faith decision chose whether or not to will to stand up (see *The Ministry of Healing,* pp. 84, 85).

Some of Paul's converts thought that eating food offered to idols was sinful. Paul knew that an idol was nothing and that offering food to an idol did not change the food in any way (1 Cor. 8; 10:14-30). However, he taught that faith required commitment in harmony with one's own conviction (Rom. 14:5). "But those who have doubts are condemned if they eat, because they do not act from faith; for whatever does not proceed from faith is sin" (verse 23).

This faith decision involved choosing whether or not to eat food presented to an idol. A person should make a faith commitment on everything that appears to be true to that individual.

Generalizing from this example and many similar ones, the subject matter of faith decisions includes everything that is apparently true. The life of faith involves commitment on whatever is supported by evidence (see *The Desire of Ages,* p. 458; *Testimonies for the Church,* vol. 3, p. 255).

Scientific truth about how to preserve and develop health is, therefore, subject matter for faith decisions. We should not limit faith decisions narrowly to the life, death, and resurrection of Jesus. If we take a broad view, thinking of Jesus Christ as the living embodiment of the totality of truth (John 14:6), all faith decisions are about Jesus Christ. In every faith decision the free gift that produces the new creation is Christ in you (Gal. 2:20).

FAITH IS PROGRESSIVE

In his classic statement Paul said that the gospel reveals God's righteousness "through faith for faith" (Rom. 1:17). In this phrase the first act of faith receives God's righteousness. This righteousness is then the base for the next act of faith. The "renewing of your minds" (Rom. 12:2) that occurs in faith improves the capacity to "discern what is the will of God" for the next faith decision.

Faith builds on faith. In the moment of making our first faith decision, we have the assurance of salvation. However, we should not claim once assured, always assured. With the assurance of righteousness "that comes through faith in Christ" (Phil. 3:9), Paul continued "straining forward" (verse 13) in the life of faith.

Every new truth learned is an opportunity for a faith decision that builds on past faith decisions. Every new health truth learned is a chance for another faith decision.

Paul wrote to the Thessalonians saying, "Your faith is growing abundantly, and the love of every one of you for one another is increasing" (2 Thess. 1:3). The members responded to each new awareness of truth with faith commitment, and grace created a corresponding increased capacity to love. Truth is infinite, and there will never come a time when we have no more truth to discover as a basis for faith decisions.

HEALTH AS ABUNDANT LIFE

Jesus said, "I came that they may have life, and have it abundantly" (John 10:10). He offers us constantly increasing abundant life. When Paul proclaimed the promise of God's righteousness "through faith for faith" (Rom. 1:17), he quoted from Habakkuk, who said, "The righteous will live by his faith" (NIV). Each increment of this abundant life comes through a faith decision and free grace.

In the Sermon on the Mount Jesus developed the spiritual significance of the law. Harboring hateful thoughts broke the commandment "You shall not murder" (Ex. 20:13; Matt. 5:21, 22) and endangered eternal life. We could formulate the commandment not to kill in a positive way by saying, *Promote life*. The scientific pursuit of health by grace through faith receives abundant life from God and furnishes a temple for the Holy Spirit, who glorifies God (1 Cor. 6:19, 20). Such scientific pursuit of health is an integral part of the abundant life of salvation by faith.

*Bible references in this chapter are from the New Revised Standard Version unless noted otherwise.

Dalton Baldwin, now retired, was professor of Christian theology at Loma Linda University, Loma Linda, California.

Chapter 12

HEAL THY NEIGHBOR
—JESUS DID!

Alberta Mazat

This chapter will draw together some of the interpersonal influences that shape the healthful functioning of the individual. We recognize that whatever influences one part of a person's makeup affects the whole being. Proceeding from this, we can look at the interactional relationships (what scholars call the social systems) within which a person lives and functions to explore their contribution to all our social health and well-being. We will consider such interpersonal relationships both in the family and in the religious, occupational, community, and health systems, and then examine how the church can relate to them.

The Family System

We can consider a healthy family relationship as a dynamic state that fosters the development and harmonious interplay of the physical, mental, social, and spiritual elements of each member. This will enable the family to reach its maximum potential while at the same time producing minimal conflict. We would want to avoid anything that hinders social development and harmonious interplay. Some of the factors contributing both to a well-functioning family and to promoting social health are as follows:

1. The nucleus of the family—the husband and wife—will choose to become a family only after careful and prayerful thought, well-informed premarital counseling, and reasonable timing. Should events alter the traditional family form and it become a single-parent family or a blended family, the church

will be prepared to minister wisely throughout the whole process as well.

2. There will be appropriate, informed socialization of children into the family system—in other words, good parenting. In a culture that does not educate individuals to understand all the social implications of child-bearing, we can expect parents to be ill-prepared to take up this task. Our church must undertake a concentrated campaign to help its members understand its importance, and then to follow through with consistent and helpful programs that highlight rearing children with self-esteem and provide the parents with the skills to make good decisions.

3. Socially healthy families are prepared to study the process of family training and to make any necessary changes in their own parenting behaviors. Research demonstrates that families operating on a model of authoritarian principles do not effectively equip their children to meet today's challenges. Children who have been nurtured in a family that employs loving discipline (versus punishment) not only exhibit better behavior, but are more likely to remain in the parents' religious faith and community.

4. Besides just being grieved by the accounts of violence in our culture, we must pay careful attention to the findings that indicate many of these incidents have their origin in authoritarian, fundamentalist homes. In fact, we have only to pay attention to the principles outlined in Scripture and in *The Adventist Home* and *Child Guidance* to realize that inspiration has always called for love, nurture, and reason to be the ideal in Seventh-day Adventist homes. We should have no roughness, violence, or neglect. The fact that it exists is lamentable, because it deeply wounds the social health of family members.

5. Seventh-day Adventist homes should be free from sexual abuse, molestation, and incest. Because such things are embarrassing and painful to talk about, we have taken the easy way out and for too long ignored them. Yet we read Jesus' dire warnings carefully preserved by Matthew (18:6), Mark (9:42), and Luke (17:2) to anyone who offends one of His little ones. We have not actively protected all of our children against this tragedy, which has such bitter, lasting, and toxic effects on social health. Even when we

have identified abusers, we have not definitively dealt with them. Many breakdowns in social health have followed in the aftermath of such tragedies.

6. To deal successfully with biases against sex, race, age, and socioeconomic status, we must first address them in the home. It is more than a lyric from a song—it is truism that "you have to be carefully taught" to be prejudiced against other persons. The family is everybody's first and most influential teacher.

This is by no means an exhaustive listing of all the family influences that effect social health. But it may serve to arouse our thinking and to help us realize that we pass negative concepts from generation to generation, impairing family health at each of its life stages. Only direct intervention can change this pattern.

The Religious System

Few denominations so consistently emphasize the importance of religious input into every area of living as does ours. Here are some representative ways in which our corporate church body could minister to the health of its members.

1. We should have a pastoral system in place to provide instruction, comfort, and guidance in all spiritual matters. This would involve not only studying "the science of salvation," but also those issues having to do with lifestyle decisions, and of the different problems that confront us during the various stages of life. Such a pastoral system would be willing to face squarely and redemptively tough issues such as divorce, infidelity, sexual deviation, violence, abuse, abortion, etc.

2. The church should affirm the equality of each child of God. Each church policy should confirm and demonstrate that it truly believes that discrimination in any form is not Christlike. When we allow differentiation in policies because of age, sex, race, or disability, the resulting feelings of inequality, inferiority, and resentment will affect the social health of a church and its members. As we consider this, we must include not only policies having to do with local church offices, but also hiring, placement, salaries, opportunities, and benefits throughout the church's organization.

3. Participation of the membership in decision-making pro-

motes social health. Openness in reporting church decisions and activities leads to trust and accountability. Members want to be assured that the church disperses its funds carefully and efficiently only after consultation with experienced and qualified personnel.

4. Church administration and officers should deal with each other along scriptural principles of justice, fairness, respect, and compassion, thus providing a practical demonstration of the gospel in action.

5. Local church members interacting in love would have a tremendous impact on the social health of the church's constituents. Understanding and support would then replace criticism and judgmentalism; warmth and caring would crowd out cold formalism; and pride of opinion would give way to open discussion— till all those observing us would exclaim, "How these Christians love one another!" Church communities that pay attention to these spiritual aspects of social health would prove irresistible to onlookers. Witnessing and evangelism would intensify as never before.

THE OCCUPATIONAL SYSTEM

The manner in which persons earn their livelihood shapes their socioeconomic status in society as well as strongly influences their emotional, physical, and social status. In God's original plan work was not only to be productive and satisfying in an atmosphere most conducive to physical benefits, but it allowed for the original inhabitants of Eden to feel their value and preciousness to their Creator. The present state of society prevents much of that from happening. But we can still be aware of the principles involved and attempt to provide some of the same components in the interest of social health.

1. We should guarantee a physically safe, protected work atmosphere. This would include not only safety of access but also a nontoxic area protected from undue crowding or noise.

2. Christian workplaces would be free from any type of harassment, including sexual harassment. There would be "safe" places to report any such problems, and when the perpetrator is known, administration would *not* respond with a token rebuke and just move the person somewhere else.

3. We would place people in positions that would reflect their abilities, knowledge, and potential. Christian employers would provide opportunity for continued growth and advancement, so that there could be an increasing sense of productivity. Dismissal would come not as a surprise, but only after all reasonable efforts to bring efficiency to a satisfactory and reasonable level had failed.

4. Compensation would match the time spent and the responsibilities assigned.

5. Benefits would provide freedom from undue concern over illness, accident, or job loss resulting from business reorganization. It would also provide vacation time, as well as daily rest periods within the work hours. Sociologists have established that such considerations make for a healthier workforce.

6. Discrimination of any type would not be present, whether overt or hidden. Relegating a whole race or gender to inferior, less respected, less remunerative positions has horrendously cost our culture economically. In terms of the effect upon feelings of hopelessness, resentment, and hostility, the price we pay is immeasurable. Resentment and anger not only get played out in broken relationships, social unrest, riots, and even warfare, but also sap the desire to relate to spiritual themes.

This brief discussion certainly does not exhaust the social implications of our work conditions, but it does point out our church's need to explore ways in which employment practices in any Seventh-day Adventist institution can follow guidelines that will lift it above the legally mandated minimum responsibility.

We could include here other social system interactions, such as those that take place in the educational, political, and legal systems. Also we could mention the community system that involves the people we live with in our neighborhoods, towns, and cities. In addition, we could explore environmental issues and the husbanding of natural resources, as well as the need for creating and preserving beauty for recreational healing through parklands and waterways. Each of these areas impinges on our social health. However, we have space to look at only one more area of concern, the area of physical health—the "right-arm issue"—and its interaction with social health.

THE MASTER'S HEALING TOUCH

THE HEALTH-CARE SYSTEM

At present few would disagree about the connection between physical and social/emotional health. Social conditions affect both physical and emotional health, and health also impinges upon social conditions. However, we should point out here that a person may be ill and still be socially healthy to an extent.

If a person has (1) a reasonable response to illness, and (2) a supportive environment, that individual can still have healthy social relationships within the family and the community. Sociologist Talcott Parsons best explains a "reasonable response" in his delineation of the sick role. He proposes that those who interact with an ill person react positively when the following are true:

- The ill person seeks recovery by going to technically competent helpers empowered by society.

- The ill person sees the condition as undesirable and wishes to recover.

- The ill person cooperates with the medical profession.

- The ill person relinquishes his/her usual roles (work, recreational, community, etc.) and is relieved of, or assisted with, family roles for the duration of the illness. In other words, we must direct all possible efforts toward preparing the patient to return to normal life as quickly as possible.

A person's social health may also be functional if he or she has a supportive environment. This would include at least several of the following:

- A nuclear family whose members are empathetic and helpful, displaying no evidence of resentment for the disorganization the illness causes.

- Extended family members who rally to provide physical and emotional support.

- Friends and neighbors who give tangible evidence of their concern by calls, cards, visits, casseroles, etc.

- Work colleagues who demonstrate their goodwill and assure that they look forward to welcoming the recovered one back to the workplace.

- Access to other social systems, such as the church, legal (if involved), insurance (it is hoped), and community resources, such as specialty support groups for specific medical conditions (e.g., Alzheimer's, muscular dystrophy, epilepsy, etc.).

- Health-care professionals (nurses, doctors, and ancillary care-givers) who see the patient as a person rather than as a case number.
- A hospital system that provides care to the whole person, practices accountability and good Samaritanism in admitting and billing, and sees the patient's needs as more important than the management's desire to head a prestigious institution.
- A medical professional whose code of ethics defines his or her objectives to the patient, and sees health care as a right rather than a reward to the privileged few.
- Medical institutions that provide working conditions already outlined under the occupational system.

Idealistic? Absolutely! Unless we constantly review such goals, the health-care experience can take a great toll on social health. Illness and health are both parts of our lives, and we are always living in a state that moves from one to the other. Even when we are well, worry and concern over possible illness can affect our social health.

Do we need to be concerned about the statistics showing that those in the lower socioeconomic groups do not receive the same quality and quantity of medical care as those more affluent? Many believe that some of the social conditions and behaviors that frustrate society today trace in part to this inequality. What would Isaiah have to say about this?

While health-care systems struggle with such issues, they also seek to cope with problems created by such advances as new reproductive technology, transplant procedures, and tissue research. How much money should be spent on the exorbitant costs for some procedures that benefit a few, while the larger part of the population lacks even routine care?

We should mention the need for an all-out push for preventative health education and its effect upon social health. Our denomination's health emphasis from its inception has stressed this need. God has given much valuable information to aid this ministry to the whole person. Yet we have spent more money and energy on healing than we have on prevention. Such knowledge put into practice could do away with much chronic and even some acute illness. Proper nutrition and good health habits, along with the rest of the "big eight" delivered to us through Ellen White (see *The Ministry of Healing,* p. 127), are an important part of the divine package that can enhance not only the physical health but the social health of all.

Alberta Mazat is a retired professor of marriage and family therapy, Loma Linda University, Loma Linda, California.

Chapter 13

WHAT DO ADVENTISTS REALLY BELIEVE ABOUT HEALTH?

Fred Hardinge, D.H.Sc., M.P.H., R.D.

The Seventh-day Adventist Church originated in an era of rapid scientific and social change. Until the latter half of the nineteenth century, however, few had a general knowledge of the principles of healthful living and treatment of disease.[1] But reform movements began to pursue better health. The Seventh-day Adventist Church is unique in that it incorporated into its theology many of these health-related reforms, something other religious organizations existing during these formative years failed to accomplish.

HEALTHFUL LIVING AND ADVENTIST THEOLOGY

Seventh-day Adventists see life as a continuing, moment-by-moment gift of God, not a state conferred at some point in the past. Accordingly, life exists only as long as this gift continues to flow from Him, the only source of life.

S. N. Haskell, an early Adventist theologian, wrote, "Every true Christian should, therefore, take a broader view of Christ's mission than merely to say, 'God forgives sins.' In forgiving of sin, it should be remembered that there is also a removing of the effects of sin, and sickness is one of these effects. Repentance toward God includes, therefore, a ceasing to transgress physical laws; and faith in Christ Jesus embraces God as the author of these laws, as well as what is termed the moral law, which lies back of all transgression, both physical and moral."[2]

Adventists, therefore, place the laws of nature alongside the moral law and believe that humanity must obey both. We should eliminate those habits that science has established as contrary to nature from the life of the sincere Christian. Ellen White supported this notion: "When men take any course which needlessly expends their vitality or beclouds their intellect, they sin against God; they do not glorify Him in their body and spirit, which are His. . . . Men and women can not violate natural law by indulging depraved appetites and lustful passions, without violating the law of God. Therefore He has permitted the light of health reform to shine upon us, that we may realize the sinfulness of breaking the laws which He has established in our very being" *(Counsels on Health,* pp. 20, 21).

The concept of the body as the temple of God (Rom. 12:1-2; 1 Cor. 3:16, 17; 6:19, 20; 10:31) is fundamental to the Adventist philosophy of health. J. N. Andrews, another early theologian, wrote, "Our bodies are the temple of the Holy Spirit. That we may truly glorify Him in our bodies, as in our spirits, how requisite that we possess in full vigor all the powers of our physical being. Thank God that this subject is now being especially set before our people."[3]

"Sinful indulgence," writes Ellen White, "defiles the body and unfits men for spiritual worship. He who cherishes the light which God has given him upon health reform has an important aid in the work of becoming sanctified through the truth, and fitted for immortality. But if he disregards that light and lives in violation of natural law, he must pay the penalty; his spiritual powers are benumbed, and how can he perfect holiness in the fear of God? . . . It is impossible for a man to present his body a living sacrifice, holy, acceptable to God, while continuing to indulge habits that are depriving him of physical, mental, and moral vigor" *(ibid.,* pp. 22, 23).

THE SANCTUARY AND HEALTH

A study of the sanctuary and its services, notably an understanding of the Day of Atonement, helps us understand the significance of true health reform. Richard M. Davidson[4] points out that we can fully appreciate the significance of the Day of Atonement only when we grasp its setting in the book of

WHAT DO ADVENTISTS BELIEVE ABOUT HEALTH?

Leviticus. The theological content of Leviticus 16 and its companion chapter, Leviticus 23, spell out the priest's rituals as well as the specific responsibilities of the congregation.

One particular duty touches Christian lifestyle and behavior. "For ancient Israel 'the affliction of soul' was regarded as a call to fasting [Ps. 35:13; Isa. 58:3, 5] and in the antitype we may see a parallel in the message of health reform."[5] In the words of Ellen White, God calls His end-time remnant to a life of true temperance that "teaches us to dispense entirely with everything hurtful and to use judiciously that which is healthful" *(Patriarchs and Prophets,* p. 562).

Ellen White extends this thought to include many areas of reform, such as diet: "There are few who realize as they should how much their habits of diet have to do with their health, their character, their usefulness in this world, and their eternal destiny" *(ibid.).*

WHAT IS "HEALTH"?

We can divide the human body into functional, support, and guidance systems. Each system contains a series of distinct units, each unit specifically designed to fulfill its precise role. It is important to note that all thought and emotion occur within a physiologically functioning organism.

ORGANIZATION OF THE HUMAN BODY
A Functional Model

Functional Units	Support Systems	Guidance Systems
• Enzymes • Cells • Organs • Systems	• Respiratory • Circulatory • Digestive • Eliminative	• Genetic • Chemical • Nervous • Mechanical

Within this immense array of chemical and biological activity that we call life, each unit is interdependent. In order for the smallest enzyme to function properly, all other functional, support, and guidance systems must work in harmony. *Health is the sum total of this exquisitely orchestrated performance—the myriads of functional units working perfectly, adequately supported, and appropriately guided.* Everything pulsating in harmony—a state of physical, mental, and spiritual peace. In the language of the space program, "all systems are go," and optimum health is the result.

When Adam and Eve chose to eat from the forbidden tree, sin entered our world, and a process of dying replaced health. When we violate the laws of our bodies, a step-by-step failure begins in the execution of one or more of the body's functions. First the quantity of output decreases, then a loss of quality of output occurs, followed by tissue damage. Disease, in its most basic definition, is damaged structures with impaired functions. When God finally abolishes sin, He will eradicate disease forever, and humanity will then enjoy unending health as He originally designed.

Physiology offers many examples of the necessity of balance for optimum function. For example, physiological systems require proper pH and temperature. If the pH or temperature varies beyond very specific limits, either high or low, it impairs the body's function or stops it altogether. Science calls those limits the biological range. Our multidimensional definition of health suggests that to achieve optimum health, we must maintain the proper biological range for body, mind, and soul. Furthermore, we must preserve balance among each major component, that is, we must complement appropriately balanced physical habits by equally balanced mental and spiritual activities.

WHY SHOULD A CHRISTIAN WORRY ABOUT HEALTH HABITS?

Teaching a set of healthful practices without reference to, or divorced from, an understanding of their impact on humanity's various dimensions has caused much misunderstanding, easily leading to guilt and anger or being perceived as an attempt to earn one's way to heaven by compliance with a specific set of do's and don'ts.

As humans, our most basic functions of life have the most resistance to the violation of physical law. Even our physical performance has great resistance to physical abuse. (The runner who lights a cigarette after completing a marathon is an example.) Mental activity is not as resistant (easily seen when a child deprived of a few hours of sleep becomes irritable and quarrelsome). Spiritual discernment, the highest level of human function, has the least tolerance to poor living habits.

That the human organism can continue to function in spite of an enormous amount of abuse testifies to the Creator's genius and love. This capacity to withstand poor habits, especially in the least-perceptible areas of life, lulls many into complacency over their habits. Yet the reality is that every wrong habit has a negative impact on one or more levels of our existence. "The brain nerves which communicate with the entire system are the only medium through which Heaven can communicate to man and affect his inmost life. Whatever disturbs the circulation of the electric currents in the nervous system lessens the strength of the vital powers, and the result is a deadening of the sensibilities of the mind" (*Testimonies for the Church,* vol. 2, p. 347).

"A pure, healthy life is most favorable for the perfection of Christian character and for the development of the powers of mind and body" (*Counsels on Health,* p. 41).

"Whatever injures the health, not only lessens physical vigor, but tends to weaken the mental and moral powers. Indulgence in any unhealthful practice makes it more difficult for one to discriminate between right and wrong, and hence more difficult to resist evil. It increases the danger of failure and defeat" (*The Ministry of Healing,* p. 128).

Satan, well aware of our physiological design, seeks to thwart God's plan to aid us in character development. Using today's moral pollution, the devil goes about his work with vigor. God desires to protect His followers from delusion by keeping our minds clear and sharp through a balanced lifestyle that avoids the harmful and judiciously uses the good. To this end He has revealed in Scripture, and amplified through the writings of Ellen White, a wonderful, scientifically validated message of healthful living.

How Should Health Principles Be Taught?

The amount of health counsel found in Scripture, Ellen White, and current scientific research may seem overwhelming, especially when a new Christian believer encounters an ardent health reformer!

How should we handle this situation? Does a person have to incorporate everything into his or her lifestyle immediately? How can one determine what is core and what is not? At what rate should he or she adopt health reform? How can a person separate nonsense from sound information—especially when sincere, well-meaning, but often ignorant and misinformed zealots promulgate the nonsense? Should cultural and geographical differences determine choices and the pace of change?

Unfortunately, those who promote good ideas in an unloving, harsh way have done a lot of damage to health reform through the years. Too frequently we approach others by attacking what we may regard as wrong habits. Such improper tactics often result in health deform!

The Bible and the writings of Ellen White reveal that the reception of truth is progressive. Paul says, "I fed you with milk, not solid food; for you were not ready for it; and even yet you are not ready" (1 Cor. 3:2, RSV). Ellen White wrote: "From the beginning of the health reform work, we have found it necessary to educate, educate, educate. . . . In teaching health reform, as in all other gospel work, we are to meet the people where they are. Until we can teach them how to prepare health reform foods that are palatable, nourishing, and yet inexpensive, we are not at liberty to present the most advanced proposition regarding health reform diet. Let the diet reform be progressive" (*Testimonies for the Church,* vol. 7, pp. 132-135).

"Of all people in the world, reformers should be the most unselfish, the most kind, the most courteous. In their lives should be seen the true goodness of unselfish deeds. The worker who manifests a lack of courtesy, who shows impatience at the ignorance or waywardness of others, who speaks hastily or acts thoughtlessly, may close the door to hearts so that he can never reach them" (*The Ministry of Healing,* p. 157).

WHAT ARE THE CORE HEALTH TEACHINGS IN THE SEVENTH-DAY ADVENTIST CHURCH?

The Seventh-day Adventist Church is known around the globe for its teachings on healthful living. An examination of the historical and current health standards accepted by the church reveal that we can divide them into two distinct categories:

1. Minimal standards required for church membership. The current *Church Manual* lists the baptismal vows that each candidate requesting baptism and membership into the church must accept. Vow 10 reads: "Do you believe that your body is the temple of the Holy Spirit; and will you honor God by caring for it, avoiding the use of that which is harmful; abstaining from all unclean foods; from the use, manufacture, or sale of alcoholic beverages; the use, manufacture, or sale of tobacco in any of its forms for human consumption; and from the misuse of or trafficking in narcotics or other drugs?"[6]

Minimal standards include abstention from tobacco, alcoholic beverages, mind-altering chemicals, and unclean flesh foods. We should note that rarely is a person disciplined for the use or abuse of these substances, although the *Church Manual* provides for such action in the case of alcohol, tobacco, and abuse of drugs, but not the use of unclean meat.

2. Other important precepts for healthful living. Growing from the recognition that not only the church but also the individual Christian is a temple for the indwelling of the Holy Spirit, the church calls Christians to observe good health habits to protect the command center of their body temples, the mind, the dwelling place of the Spirit.[7] For more than 100 years the Adventist Church has stressed the importance of proper health habits for the Christian. These habits—physical, mental, and spiritual—while not defined specifically, are implied by vow 11 as stated in the *Church Manual:* "Do you know and understand the fundamental Bible principles as taught by the Seventh-day Adventist Church? Do you purpose, by the grace of God, to fulfill His will by ordering your life in harmony with these principles?"[8]

Although they are not considered mandatory for church membership, we should consider these general principles as essential for proper spiritual development and growth, as well as important in the prevention of disease and the restoration of health. The teaching of such habits is rooted in the moral imperatives of Scripture, which seek the wholeness intended by our Creator.

From this perspective perhaps we should consider these broad, general principles more important than the minimal standards outlined in the *Church Manual*.

The best expression of the general areas covered by this category is: "Pure air, sunlight, abstemiousness, rest, exercise, proper diet, the use of water, trust in divine power—these are the true remedies. Every person should have a knowledge of nature's remedial agencies and how to apply them. . . . Those who persevere in obedience to [natural] laws will reap the reward in health of body and health of mind" *(The Ministry of Healing,* p. 127).

Currently many refer to the eight broad principles by terms such as the "Eight Doctors," "Nature's Eight Remedies," "The Golden Eight," and NEWSTART. When viewed as general guidelines for good health, this list of eight areas is quite inclusive. We may include mental health habits within a broad definition of rest and trust in divine power. A lifestyle patterned on these eight principles will be complete, balanced, effective, economical, and scientifically sound. When understood properly, they form the foundation for a healthy Christian lifestyle. Because of their general nature, they apply to all areas of the globe, notwithstanding geographic, economic, cultural, and social differences. Only the Creator could have authored such a complete, yet universally applicable, standard!

The method and attitude surrounding the teaching of health practices within the church and community determine to a large extent their degree of acceptance. To simply teach a list of good health practices with biblical, Ellen White, and scientific backup is not enough. We must present the principles of health reform in the context of their contribution to the Christian experience and goals.

A "Ladder of Health" approach furnishes a conceptual framework to develop individual habits. The base sustaining the ladder includes two components: commitment to Christ and a desire to grow in Him. Without this foundation, healthful living only produces healthy sinners. With it, health reform centers in Jesus and the development of character.

Scripture and the writings of Ellen White contain no checklist of necessary habits to begin a Christian life. In fact, a relationship with Christ often must be established before the minimum can be successfully experienced in a person's life. The power to change comes from Christ Himself.

Once a person has made a commitment to Jesus and the process of Christian growth has begun, what comes next? It seems clear that each Christian should achieve the minimum standard, the core, in his or her life. Following that would come a steady, continual growth in all areas of Christian life, including healthful habits.

The Ladder of Health

Broad Principles	Minimum Core	Some Specific Concerns
• Good nutrition • Exercise • Water and pure air • Avoid toxic input • Sunlight • Rest • Trust in God	• No alcoholic beverages • No tobacco • No unclean meats • Sexual purity	• Stress control • Minimal use of chemical therapeutics (drugs) • Tea, coffee, and similar drinks • Gluttony • Vegetarian diet • Toxic input: TV, movies • Weight control • Use of spices

The minimum standards should be placed at the lowest rungs of the ladder. Yet their exact order will differ for each individual. Certain points of the broad principles may be included prior to all of the core principles. Each person's experience will be different. He or she must seek God's will in selecting the good habits to apply to life by praying, "Lord, what will You have me to do next?" Then, as the Holy Spirit reveals the next item, it will go on the next rung and be implemented through God's help.

This approach provides flexibility and latitude to every Christian. It places the responsibility of deciding what and when in the hands of the individual, allowing the Holy Spirit freedom to prompt him or her according to his or her stage of understanding and development. The work of the health educator is to "educate, educate, educate," explaining the whys and wherefores, but leaving the responsibility for growth and implementation to each individual person and the Holy Spirit.

CONCLUSION

God summons Christians to adopt a unique lifestyle, not for the sake of being different, but because God calls them to live by principle. This lifestyle, designed by the Creator, enables them to reach their full potential as His creation, giving them the greatest efficiency in His service. God's laws, including the laws of health, are not arbitrary, but are designed to enable us to enjoy life to the fullest.

Our behavior and our spirituality have a close relationship, yet we can never earn salvation simply by making good health choices. The development of a Christian health-style is progressive, involving a lifelong union with Christ. Holy living is nothing less than a daily yielding of the will to Christ's control and a daily conformity to His teachings as He reveals them to us in our Bible study and prayer. This is true health reform—health reform as it centers in Jesus Christ. Christian health behavior is the natural fruit of salvation and is rooted in what Christ accomplished for us at Calvary.

---

[1] Dores E. Robinson, *The Story of Our Health Message* (Nashville: Southern Pub. Assn., 1955), pp. 13-27.

[2] Stephen N. Haskell, "Christ the Healer From the Beginning," *The Medical Missionary,* May 1891, p. 13.

[3] John N. Andrews, in *Review and Herald,* Oct. 25, 1864, p. 176.

[4] Richard M. Davidson, "The Good News of Yom Kippur," *Journal of the Adventist Theological Society* 2, No. 2 (1991): 13.

[5] *Ibid.,* p. 16.

[6] *The Seventh-day Adventist Church Manual* (Hagerstown, Md.: Review and Herald Pub. Assn., 1995), p. 31.

[7] See *Seventh-day Adventists Believe . . . A Biblical Exposition of 27 Fundamental Doctrines* (Washington, D.C.: Ministerial Association, General Conference of Seventh-day Adventists), pp. 280, 281.

[8] *Church Manual,* p. 31.

Fred Hardinge is director of the Total Health Foundation, Yakima, Washington.